Interactions II
Workbook

Interactions II

A Cognitive Approach to Beginning Chinese

Workbook

Jennifer Li-chia Liu
劉力嘉

Margaret Mian Yan
嚴棉

Indiana University Press
Bloomington and Indianapolis

This book is a publication of

INDIANA UNIVERSITY PRESS
601 North Morton Street
Bloomington, IN 47404-3797 USA

http://www.indiana.edu/~iupress

Telephone orders 800-842-6796
Fax orders 812-855-7931
Orders by email iuporder@indiana.edu

The paper used in this publication meets the minimum
requirements of American National Standard for Information
Science—Permanence of Paper for Printed Library
Materials, ANSI Z39.48-1984.

MANUFACTURED IN THE UNITED STATES OF AMERICA

Cataloging information is available from the Library of Congress.

By Margaret Mian Yan and Jennifer Li-chia Liu
ISBN 0-253-21122-0 paperback (Interactions I)
ISBN 0-253-21202-2 paperback (Interactions I: Workbook)

By Jennifer Li-chia Liu and Margaret Mian Yan
ISBN 0-253-21123-9 paperback (Interactions II)
ISBN 0-253-21203-0 paperback (Interactions II: Workbook)
ISBN 0-253-21201-4 paperback (Interactions I & II: Teacher's Manual)

2 3 4 5 08 07 06 05 04

Contents

Preface

This **Workbook** is designed to complement the student text ***Interactions II: A Cognitive Approach to Beginning Chinese*** and to give students of diverse background a variety of practice with spoken as well as written Chinese.

All the exercises are written based on the communicative approach to language teaching and arranged to facilitate the acquisition of discrete language points and practice in all four language skills. In addition, the awareness of cultural differences is encouraged. Thus whenever possible, we have contextualized the exercises by providing a realistic and meaningful situation for the use of Chinese in the hopes of establishing a link between language study and reality.

From Lesson 14 through Lesson 23, we include both language-focused discrete practice and skill-oriented synthesized task. The exercises, divided into seven sections, follow the sequence: Vocabulary, Character, Grammar, Listening, Speaking, Reading, and Writing.

It is recommended that the workbook exercises be assigned *selectively* after each lesson in the student text is presented. An array of exercises is created to meet students' various needs and to lessen teachers' preparation time. For example, a speaking proficient student like many ethnic Chinese should be asked to work more on reading and writing than on speaking and listening. The Speaking and Grammar section can be done in class. The Listening section can be saved for quizzes. The section on characters and writing can be used as homework. In sum, students are *not* expected to complete all the exercises in each lesson.

The Listening sections are designed to be used with the accompanying audiotapes. The tapescripts for the Listening section recorded on cassettes as well as the answer key for some exercises are given in the teacher's manual. Some visuals in the book are created in Corel Draw and some adapted from the clip arts in Corel Gallery by Corel Corporation, 1994. Most of the authentic reading materials included in the Reading section are from the World Journal 世界日報 Shìjiè Rìbào published in New York (1997) and first/second grade reader 國語課本 Guóyǔ Kèběn compiled by National Institute for Compilation and Translation 國立編譯館 Guólì Biānyìguǎn in Taiwan (1996/1997). We would like to express our sincere gratitude to these two institutions for their permission to include their materials in our workbook. We would like also to thank the following business firms/companies for allowing us to use their advertisements in the workbook and helping students to enhance their Chinese reading competence: 永聰軒 Chung's Cantonese & Mandarin [Cuisine], 世界書局 W. J. Bookstore, 中國書店 Central China Book Company , 東方職業介紹所 Atlantic Employment Agency, 大通電訊 Primus Telecommunications Inc., 上海四五六菜館 Moon Palace Restaurant, and 健安堂藥材公司 Ken On Tong Herbs, Inc., 華美中醫

康復中心 Hoami [Traditional Chinese Medicine Recovery Center], 李富華汽車維修中心 Vinnes Auto Service Center, and 藍天旅遊 Wings Travel and Tours. Last but not least, we would like to thank Kenneth Goodall, Paul Manfredi, and Lara Ingeman for their editorial help.

                                                                                    The Authors

第十四課　寒假過得怎麼樣？

I. Vocabulary

A. Write on or around the pictures any words they suggest.

1.    2.    3.

B. Complete the crossword puzzle with the cues given.

Across	Down
2. to be fun	1. to sleep through the day
4. cannot walk	2. long time no see
5. to see one's older sister	3. gym

C. Choose the appropriate word to complete the following sentences.

1. Tā bù xǐ.huān dǎ (xiàowài, chángtú, chángduǎn) diànhuà huíjiā, yīn.wèi diànhuà .lǐ shuō.bùliǎo shén.me.

   他不喜歡打(校外、長途、長短)電話回家，因爲電話裏說不了什麼。

2. Wǒ huā .le yì zhěng tiān .de xuě, lèi .de (zǒuqǐlái, shuō.bùliǎo, zǒu.búdòng) .le.

   我滑了一整天的雪，累得(走起來、說不了、走不動)了。

3. Nǐ děi gěi nǐ fùmǔ xiěxìn, (nánguài, miǎn.de, dǎsuàn) tā.men dānxīn.

   你得給你父母寫信，(難怪、免得、打算)他們擔心。

4. Tā (píngcháng, lìkè, gāng) bù xǐ.huān dāi zài sùshè .lǐ.

   他(平常、立刻、剛)不喜歡待在宿舍裏。

II. Characters

Hàn zì	爸	媽	姐	弟	全	身	平	常	如	果
Notes	bà dad 8	mā mom 13	jiě elder sister 8	dì younger brother 7	quán entire 6	shēn body 7	píng flat 5	cháng common 8	rú if, as if 6	guǒ fruit 8
1										
2										
3										
4										
5										
6										

	Compound/Phrase/Sentence/Journal/Memory Aid
爸	
媽	
姐	
弟	
全	
身	
平	
常	
如	
果	

Hàn zì	動	腦	信	用	久	候	原	房	鞋	第
Notes	dòng move, act 11	nǎo brain 9	xìn to believe 9	yòng to use 5	jiǔ long 3	hòu to wait 10	yuán original 10	fǎng house 8	xié shoe 15	dì ordinal prefix 11
1										
2										
3										
4										
5										
6										

	Compound/Phrase/Sentence/Journal/Memory Aid
動	
腦	
信	
用	
久	
候	
原	
房	
鞋	
第	

SVO

III. Grammar

A Major Sentence Patterns

1. The post-verbal preposition 在

| S (不)(要/想/喜歡) V₁ 在 Place (V₂O) | S (AuxV) V₁ at Place (V₂O) |

1. 你以後想住在哪兒？

   _____

2. 你喜歡坐在什麼地方看書？

   _____

3. 寒假的時候你想待在哪兒？爲什麼？

   _____

2. Question words as indefinites

S 哪兒/什麼地方 都 去過了	S has been in everywhere
S 哪兒/什麼地方 都/也 不/沒 去	S doesn't/didn't go to anywhere
S 什麼 N 都 AuxV V	S AuxV V everything
S 什麼 N 都 V 過了	S has V-ed everything
S 什麼 (N) 都/也 不/沒 V	S doesn't/didn't VO (at all)

1. 你昨天做了什麼？

   _____

2. 聽說你去過很多地方，對嗎？

   _____

3. 你想買什麼禮物送你弟弟？

   _____

3. The verb 給

S (沒/不) 給 Oᵢ Od.	S give Oᵢ Od
S (沒/不) V Od 給 Oᵢ	S VO to Oᵢ
S (沒/不) 給 Oᵢ V Od.	S VOd for Oᵢ

1. 生日的時候，你父母給了你什麼東西？

　　_____

2. 你今天晚上要寫信給誰？

　　_____

3. 你的朋友要給你做飯嗎？

　　_____

4.　一 ...就 ... construction

S 一 $V_1 O_1$ (S) 就 $V_2 O_2$	As soon as S $V_1 O_1$ (S) $V_2 O_2$

1. 你一上課就覺得怎麼樣？

　　_____

2. 你一放假就想做什麼？

　　_____

3. 他一看書就覺得怎麼樣？

　　_____

5.　Durative time expressions

S (VO) V 了　　　Time-Spent (了)	S did (has done) V O for Time-Spent
S　　　V 了/過　Time-Spent (的) O	S did/has done　V O for Time-Spent
S (AuxV)V　　　Time-Spent (的) O	S (will/shall)　　V O for Time-Spent
S Time-Spent 沒/不　V O	S won't/didn't　VO for Time-Spent

1. 你昨天晚上看了多久的電視？

　　_____

2. 你今天聽錄音聽了幾個小時？

　　_____

3. 你幾天沒練習說中文了？

　　_____

6. Verbs with extent complements

S (VO) V 得 怎麼樣？ S (VO) V 得 Comp	After Ving O, what happened to S? After Ving O, S was so... that...

1. 他昨天晚上唱歌唱得怎麼樣？

   _____

2. 你週末寫報告寫得怎麼樣？

   _____

3. 你游泳 (yóuyǒng, to swim) 游得怎麼樣？

   _____

7. The co-verb 跟

A (AuxV) 跟 B V O	A (AuxV) VO with B
A (不/沒/別) 跟 B V O	A (not) VO with B

1. 你的中文是跟誰學的？

   _____

2. 你的車是跟誰買的？

   _____

3. 你寒假的時候跟誰去看電影了？

   _____

 # IV. Listening

1. Where did Xiao Wang go during the winter break?
   a. To see a movie.
   b. To ski.
   c. To skate.
   d. To fish.

2. Is the event fun?
   a. It's very boring.
   b. It's O.K.
   c. It's extremely fun.
   d. It's scary.

3. Where did B spend his Christmas?
   a. At his dormitory.
   b. At a friend's house.
   c. At home.
   d. At school.

4. What was B doing on Christmas Eve?
   a. Watching TV all day long.
   b. Playing basketball all day long.
   c. Playing basketball in the afternoon and watching TV at night.
   d. Watching TV in the afternoon and playing basketball at night.

5. What gift did Xiao Lin's older sister receive?
   a. A pair of jeans.
   b. A pair of shoes.
   c. A pair of gloves.
   d. A pair of socks.

6. What gift did B's older brother receive?
   a. A shirt.
   b. A pair of boots.
   c. A pair of gloves.
   d. A pair of socks.

 V. Speaking

A. Talk about yourself
   Use the following questions as cues.
   1. 你寒假過得怎麼樣？有沒有上哪兒去玩兒？

   2. 你喜歡睡懶覺嗎？你都什麼時候睡懶覺？

   3. 你喜歡滑雪嗎？你滑雪滑得怎麼樣？你都上哪兒去滑雪？

   4. 耶誕節的時候，你們全家人做了什麼？你收到什麼禮物？你送別人什麼禮物？

B. Talk about cultural differences
    Interview a classmate of yours from another country with the questions like:
    1. Do you observe Christmas in your country? How do you do that?
    2. Do you observe other religious holidays? How do you do that?
    3. On what occasions will people exchange gifts? What kinds of gifts are being exchanged?
    4. What do people do on vacations like winter break?

C. The best place
    You enjoy skiing (or other leisure activities). Talk to your classmate and find out where is
    the best place to ski in the States. You may ask questions like: 在美國的什麼地方滑雪
    最好？

VI. Reading

A. Read the Text
    Check your comprehension of the lesson dialogue by answering the following questions.

 1. Lǐ Míng hánjià .de shí.hòu, shàng nǎr qù .le?   李明寒假的時候，上哪兒去了？

    _____

 2. Wèishén.me Lǐ Míng gěi fùmǔ xiěxìn？   為什麼李明給父母寫信？

    _____

 3. Xiǎo Lǐ wèishén.me bù dǎ diànhuà huíjiā?   小李為什麼不打電話回家？

    _____

 4. Wáng Huá yě cháng xiě xìn huíjiā .ma?   王華也常寫信回家嗎？為什麼？
     Wèishén.me?

    _____

 5. Wáng Huá hánjià .de shí.hòu, zuò .le shén.me?   王華寒假的時候，做了什麼？

    _____

 6. Nǐ xiǎng Xiǎo Wáng xǐ.huān huáxuě .ma?   你想小王喜歡滑雪嗎？為什麼？
     Wèishén.me?

    _____

 7. Lín Měiyīng hánjià .de shí.hòu, dào péng.yǒu jiā   林美英寒假的時候，到朋友家過
     guòjié .le .ma? Tā shì zěn.me guò Yēdànjié .de?   節了嗎？她是怎麼過耶誕節的？

    _____

8. Wèishén.me Xiǎo Lín xǐ.huān qù tǐyùguǎn duàn.liàn? Xiǎo Wáng yě duàn.liàn .ma?　　爲什麼小林喜歡去體育館鍛練？小王也鍛練嗎？

---

9. Xiǎo Lǐ kàn.jiàn Xiǎo Wáng, Xiǎo Lín .de shí.hòu, tā.men zhèng yào shàng nǎr qù? Wèishén.me?　　小李看見小王、小林的時候，她們正要上哪兒去？爲什麼？

B. Read the Authentic Material
   1. Read the following story[1] and answer the questions.

      a. Who wrote this story? _____

      b. Why did the author want to give _____ a gift?

      _____

      c. What was Father's suggestion? _____

      d. What kind of gift was presented by the author? _____

送給媽媽的禮物

母親節就要到了，我們每個人都想送給媽媽一樣禮物。送什麼好呢？

爸爸說：「只要是自己做的，媽媽就會喜歡。」

我畫了一朵小紅花，上面寫的是：

媽媽：您那麼忙，我要幫您做事。這朵美麗的小紅花送給您。

母親節快樂

女兒 小美

弟弟不會畫，也不會寫，他說：「誰來幫我寫？就說我要帶媽媽到動物園去，請媽媽騎大象。」

大家聽了都笑了。

[1] This is from 國民小學一年級上學期國語課本. By 國立編譯館, 台北, 1997.

VII. Writing

A. Unscramble the words to make meaningful sentences.

1. 不是／每天／電視／對著／就是／他／睡懶覺

2. 電話／時間／只好／寫信／給爸爸媽媽／打長途／沒有／我

3. 打算／我們／到山上去／寒假的時候／滑雪

4. 他媽媽／原來／他中文說得／是中國人／很好／難怪

B. You are on vacation. Write a postcard to a friend describing what you do. Use the patterns

1. S 什麼都(沒/不)...   3. S V了/過 Time-Spent (的) O
2. S 一... 就...   4. S VO V得 Comp.

第十五課 這個房子一定很貴吧？

 ## I. Vocabulary

A. Look at the following picture and fill in the appropriate new words in pinyin.

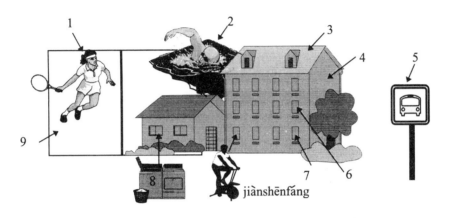

jiànshēnfáng

B. Explain the meaning of the following words in Chinese.

1. chēzhàn　　　車站　　等公車來的地方 _____
2. xìnyòngkǎ　　信用卡　_____
3. dìngjīn　　　定金　　_____
4. fángdōng　　房東　　_____
5. bāo shuǐdiàn　包水電　_____

C. Complete the paragraph by filling in the blanks with the appropriate words.

Hints　放、累死、一定、方便、支票、搬、歇、安靜、整理

我的朋友最近搬到校外住。他說雖然校外很舒服，很 _____₁，但是_____₂
一次家很不容易，快把他_____₃了。他_____₄了一個星期，才把東西
_____₅好。他說他先_____₆幾天，下個禮拜就請我去看看。他家附近有很
多有意思的書店，買書很 _____₇，我一定會喜歡的。可是我想我不應該把
我的_____₈帶去，因為我逛了書店，_____₉會把錢都花光(huāguāng 'to spend
all')的。

II. Characters

Hàn zì	知	道	吵	念	搬	進	空	樓	左	右
Notes	zhī to know 8	dào way 13	chǎo to quarrel 7	niàn to think of 8	bān to move 13	jìn enter 13	kòng free time 8	lóu building 15	zuǒ left 5	yòu right 5
1										
2										
3										
4										
5										
6										

Compound/Phrase/Sentence/Journal/Memory Aid

知

道

吵

念

搬

進

空

樓

左

右

Hàn zì	旁	邊	把	站	累	死	現	收	付	百
Notes	páng side 10	biān side 19	bǎ M 7	zhàn to stand 10	lèi tired 11	sǐ to die 6	xiàn now 11	shōu to receive 6	fù to pay 5	bǎi a hundred 6
1										
2										
3										
4										
5										
6										

	Compound/Phrase/Sentence/Journal/Memory Aid
旁	
邊	
把	
站	
累	
死	
現	
收	
付	
百	

III. Grammar

A Major Sentence Patterns

1. 把 construction

S (沒/不/別) 把 O V complement	S (doesn't/didn't) do... to O

1. 你把自己的照片掛在哪兒？

_____

2. 我把電視放在廚房嗎？

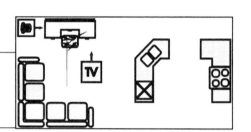

_____

3. 我把什麼放在客廳？

_____

2. Verbs with directional complements

2.1 Verbs with single directional complements

搬 bān	來/去	to move here/there
拿 ná	來/去	to bring over here/there
走 zǒu	來/去	to walk over here/there
跑 pǎo	來/去	to run over here/there
上 shàng	來/去	to go up here/there
下 xià	來/去	to go down here/there
進 jìn	來/去	to enter here/there

1. 你現在住('stay')在哪兒？是什麼時候搬去那兒的？

_____

2. 從你住的地方走來學校要三十分鐘嗎？跑來呢？

_____

3. 老師要你明天把什麼帶來？

_____

2.2 Verbs with double directional complements

搬 bān	進來 /進去	to move over here/there
放 fàng	進來 /進去	to put over here/there
拿 ná	進來 /進去	to bring...in/out
拿 ná	上 去/ 下 來	to bring...up/down
走 zǒu	進來 /進去	to walk into/out
跑 pǎo	進來 /進去	to run into/out
穿 chuān	上 去	to wear, to put on (clothes)
脫 tuō	下 來	to take (clothes) off
戴 dài	上 去	to put (jewelry, hat, glasses) on
拿 ná	下 來	to take (jewelry, hat, glasses) off
寫 xiě	下 來	to write/take (notes) down
記 jì	下 來	to write/record...down

1. 她把我的書怎麼了？

_____

 2. 他把我的照片怎麼了？

_____

3. 我的狗在哪兒？

_____

4. 進屋子的時候，你應該怎麼樣？

_____

5. 外頭很冷，你應該怎麼樣？

_____

6. 上課的時候，你應該做什麼？ (Write down what the teacher said.)

_____

7. 你不在的時候，有人給你打電話，要你打回去。(Did you write down his phone number?)

_____

2.3 Resultative verbs with directional complements

Actual form	回來/回去	huí.lái/ huí.qù	to come/go back
	進來/進去	jìn.lái/ jìn.qù	to come/go in
	上來/上去	shàng.lái/ shàng.qù	to come/go up
Positive potential form	回得來/回得去	huí.delái/ huí.dequ	can come/go back
	進得來/進得去	jìn.delái/ jìn.dequ	can come/go in
	上得來/上得去	shàng.delái/ shàng.dequ	can come/go up
Negative potential form	回不來/回不去	huí.bulái/ huí.buqù	cannot come/go back
	進不來/進不去	jìn.bulái/ jìn.buqù	cannot come/go in
	上不來/上不去	shàng.bulái/ shàng.buqù	cannot come/go up

1. 你現在去 Indianapolis 三點回得來嗎？

_____

2. 你想那個屋子他進得去進不去？

_____

　　　　　　3. 這兒你上得來嗎？

_____

3. Place words

X 旁邊兒	side of X/next to X
X 左邊兒	left side of X/to the left of X
X 右邊兒	right side of X/to the right of X
X 前邊兒/前頭兒	front side of X/in front of X
X 後邊兒/後頭兒	back side of X/behind X
X 上(邊兒)/上(頭兒)	upper side of X/on top of X
X 下(邊兒)/下(頭兒)	lower side of X/underneath of X

Read the following and draw a picture accordingly.

1. 公寓左邊兒有個公車站，右邊有游泳池，前邊有個網球場，後邊有很多樹(shù 'tree')。樹的上邊有很多鳥，下邊還有一隻狗(gǒu 'dog')。

B Usage of Common Phrases

1. The particle ... 的話

(如果/要是) S V (O) 的話	If S V (O)

1. 如果你是老師的話，你會做些什麼？不會做些什麼？

_____

2. 如果你想去中國的話，你得做什麼？

_____

3. 如果你想搬到校外的話，你應該做些什麼？

_____

2. The particle 吧

S... 吧？	S... , I suppose/I guess

1. 我學中文以前，常 (cháng 'often') 想→_____

2. 我來美國以前，常想→_____

3. 我去中國以前，常想→_____

3. 知道 vs. 認識

S₁ 知道 [S₂ (Neg) V O] S₁ 不知道 [S₂ V-not-V O] S₁ 不知道 [QW Question] 　　　(information/fact/matter)	S₁ knows (that)... S₁ doesn't know [(if)...] S₁ doesn't know [QW Question]
S (不) 認識　　O 　　(person/character/word)	S (doesn't) know (the person) S (doesn't) recognize/comprehend (the character/ word)

1. 你知道這兒有空房沒有？

_____

2. 你知道樓上的房客吵不吵？ (They just moved in. I don't know yet.)

_____

3. _____

(We haven't seen each other for some time. Do you still know me?)

開玩笑！咱們是老朋友了。

4. _____

(Do you know this character 淼 ?)

開玩笑！我就學了半年的中文。

 IV. Listening

1. What kind of apartment does A want?
   a. One-bedroom apartment.
   b. Two-bedroom apartment.
   c. Three-bedroom apartment.

2. How much is the rent for the apartment?
   a. $600
   b. $500
   c. $100

3. What did A ask B to do?
   a. To bring the books into the house.
   b. To bring the pictures into the house.
   c. To bring the TV set into the house.
   d. To bring the clothes into the house.

4. Where does A want B to put the books?
   a. Living room.
   b. Bedroom.
   c. Family room.
   d. Study.

5. Draw a sketch of the apartment described.

V. Speaking

A. Talk about yourself
   Use the following questions as cues.
   1. 你現在住在哪兒？你住的地方好不好？有什麼設備(shèbèi 'facilities')？

   2. 你的屋子裏有些什麼東西、家俱(jiājù 'furniture')？都放在哪兒？

   3. 你的房租貴不貴？你一個月付多少錢？包不包水電？

   4. 你搬過家没有？你喜不喜歡搬家？為什麼？

B. Expressing viewpoints
   Discuss with your classmates the following questions:
   1. Is it better to use cash or credit cards to shop?
   2. Which floor in an apartment building is best? Is it better to live upstairs or downstairs?
   3. Is it better to live on campus (校內 xiàonài) or off campus (校外 xiàowài)?

C. Check out an apartment
   You have seen an advertisement in the paper for a furnished apartment and you may want to
   rent it. Call the manager and ask him/her to describe it (including size, rooms, furniture,
   price, etc.). Then find out how to get there so that you can go and see it.

D. Rent a place
   Talk to your Chinese friends to find out how one rents a house or an apartment in China or
   Taiwan. Describe what one has to do.

VI. Reading

A. Read the Text
   Check your comprehension of the lesson dialogue by answering the following questions.

   1. Wáng Huá jué.de xiàowài .de gōngyù   王華覺得校外的公寓怎麼樣？
       zěn.me yàng? Wèishén.me?   為什麼？

   _____

   2. Guǎnlǐyuán dài Lín Měiyīng, Wáng Huá qù   管理員帶林美英、王華去看空房
       kàn kōngfáng, nà jiān wū.zi zěn.meyàng?   ，那間房子怎麼樣？

   _____

3. Guǎnlǐyuán shuō rúguǒ Lín Měiyīng, Wáng Huá yào bānjìn.lái .de huà, qián zěn.me fù? Fù duō.shǎo?

管理員說如果林美英、王華要搬進來的話，錢怎麼付？付多少？

_____

4. Lín Měiyīng, Wáng Huá fù .le dìngjīn méi.yǒu? Shì zěn.me fù .de?

林美英、王華付了定金沒有？是怎麼付的？

_____

5. Lín Měiyīng, Wáng Huá wèishén.me xiǎng bān.dào xiàowài zhù?

林美英、王華為什麼想搬到校外住？

_____

6. Guǎnlǐyuán shuō tā.men .de fáng.zi zěn.meyàng?

管理員說他們的房子怎麼樣？

_____

7. Wáng Huá bāng Měiyīng shén.me máng? Wèishén.me Měiyīng bú zìjǐ zuò?

王華幫美英什麼忙？為什麼美英不自己做？

_____

8. Měiyīng ràng Wáng Huá bǎ huàr fàng zài nǎr? Wèishén.me?

美英讓王華把畫兒放在哪兒？為什麼？

_____

9. Wáng Huá zěn.me shuō "zìjǐ bù néng zài bān dōng.xī .le?"

王華怎麼說「自己不能再搬東西了」？

_____

B. Read the Authentic Material
   1. Read the advertisement and figure out:

      a. How many stories does this house have?

      _____

      b. How many bedrooms does it have?

      _____

      c. What is the surname of the owner?

      _____

吉屋自售

芝城南邊兩層屋AS is $83,000可議價，地區好。樓下店鋪，1千平方呎，全土庫，後院及車房。2樓3睡房，光線充足。離唐人街5分鐘車程，離市中心15分鐘車程近Dominick市場。地址：2909 S. Archer Chicago IL: 電話：

312-838-4500   王

餐館吉售
位於Kenosha, WI.法院
、警局、醫院及辦公室
。東主年邁急退休。請
電詢，看店。

414-333-8282

2. Read the advertisement on the left and figure out which state the restaurant is located in? _____

3. If you are interested in buying the restaurant advertised on the right, what should you do?

餐館出讓
位印州熱鬧中心，
地區好，新開張餐
館出讓，有意者來
電

219-372-5321

_____

_____

_____

_____

VII. Writing

A. Unscramble the words to make meaningful sentences.

1. 這個／我們／把／有／考試kǎoshì／我們／星期／忙máng死了／三個

2. 畫huà的／他／把／畫兒huàr／掛guà／我／在牆qiáng上

3. 有／那間／旁邊兒pángbiānr／公寓yù／網球場wǎngqiúchǎng／一個

4. 請／我的／你／把／整理zhěnglǐ好／書

5. 他／就／一進門／我們的照片／看見

B. Your wallet (錢包 qiánbāo) is missing.
Write a list of all the things you have
done this morning. Detail each
activity and see if you can figure out
where you might have lost your wallet.
Use the *bǎ* construction and the words
provided in the chart below.

Action verb	Object
吃	三明治 sānmíngzhì
喝	咖啡
穿 chuān	大衣
掛 guà	照片 zhàopiàn
搬 bān	電視 diànshì
開	車

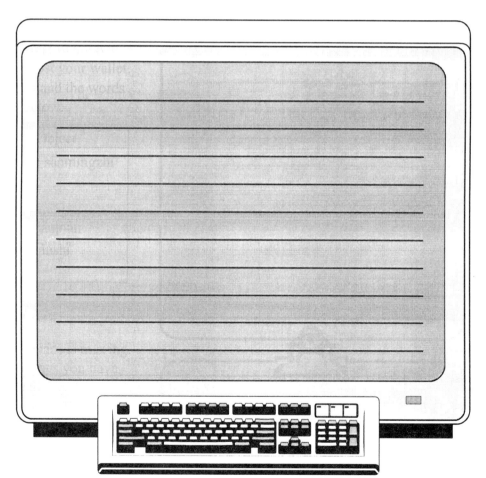

C. Write an e-mail
message looking
for a roommate
who should be a
non-smoking
male graduate
student. Include
a brief descrip-
tion of your
apartment/ house
and outline other
advantages such
as (1) cheap rent
including
utilities, (2) close
to the bus line,
and (3) quiet
neighborhood.
Also indicate
how people can
contact you if
they want to take
a look at the
place first.

第十六課 你們住得還習慣嗎？

I. Vocabulary

A. Look at the following picture and fill in the appropriate new words in pinyin.

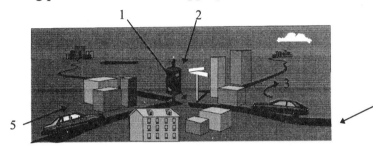

B. Word power

List as many words as you can that share the second character of the following compounds.

1.	晚會	年會	舞會	同學會
2.	球迷	_____	_____	_____
3.	旁邊	_____	_____	_____
4.	孔子	_____	_____	_____
5.	中文	_____	_____	_____
6.	吃完	_____	_____	_____

C. Choose the appropriate word to complete the following sentences.

1. Tā.men míng.tiān yào (dǎsuàn, qìngzhù, jǔbàn) Zhōng.guó xīnnián, nǐ lái bù lái?

   她們明天要(打算、慶祝、舉辦)中國新年，你來不來？

2. Nǐ.men (jiārén, quán, liǎng) bié (pà, zhù, xiē), wǒ.men yídìng huì lái bāngmáng .de.

   你們(家人、全、倆)別(怕、住、歇)，我們一定會來幫忙的。

3. Wǒ.men dào .le méi.yǒu? Zhèr (yòushì, dāngrán, jiù.shì) .le.

   我們到了沒有？這兒(又是、當然、就是)了。

4. Wǒ.men gāng bān .le xīnjiā. (Gōngxǐ a, hǎo jiǔ bú jiàn a, yǒu shén.me hǎo bān .de)!

   我們剛搬了新家。(恭喜啊、好久不見啊、有什麼好搬的)！

II. Characters

Hàn zì	又	往	街	路	容	易	習	慣	怕	受
Notes	yòu again 2	wàng to, toward 8	jiē street 12	lù road 13	róng contain 10	yì easy 8	xí to learn 11	guàn be used to 14	pà be afraid 8	shòu to receive 8
1										
2										
3										
4										
5										
6										

Compound/Phrase/Sentence/Journal/Memory Aid

又	
往	
街	
路	
容	
易	
習	
慣	
怕	
受	

Hàn zì	影	響	王	住	幫	管	花	謝	孩	夠
Notes	yǐng shadow 15	xiǎng loudly 21	wáng king 4	zhù to live 7	bāng to help 17	guǎn to control 14	huā flower 8	xiè to thank 17	hái child 9	gòu enough 11
1										
2										
3										
4										
5										
6										

	Compound/Phrase/Sentence/Journal/Memory Aid
影	
響	
王	
住	
幫	
管	
花	
謝	
孩	
夠	

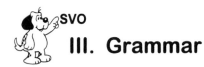

III. Grammar

Ⓐ Major Sentence Patterns

1. A 對 B 有影響 / B 受 A 的影響

A 對 B 有(很大的)影響	A has (great) influence on B
A 對 B 的影響很大	A has great influence on B
A 對 B 沒(有)影響	A has no influence on B
A 對 B 一點兒影響 都/也 沒有	A has no influence on B at all
B 受 A 的影響	B is/has been influenced by A
B 沒/不會受 A 的影響	B was not/won't be influenced by A

1. 什麼對你有很大的影響？誰對你的影響很大？

_____

2. 電視和流行音樂對你有影響嗎？

_____

3. 你受誰的影響開始學中文？

_____

2. 又...又... construction

S 又 SV₁ 又 SV₂	S is both Adj₁ and Adj₂
S 又 (AuxV) VP₁ 又 (AuxV) VP₂	S (AuxV) does both VP₁ and VP₂

1. 你為什麼想搬到校外住？

_____

2. 為什麼你受不了他(你的同屋兒、同學)？

_____

3. 如果可以的話，你想養什麼寵物(chǒngwù 'pet')？

_____

B Usage of Common Phrases

1. 往 X V expression

往 X V	V toward X
往東走	walk toward the east
往西拐	turn to the west
往南轉	turn to the south
往北看	look to the north
往右滑	ski/slide to the right
往左跑	run toward the left
往上爬	climb upward/toward the top
往下走	walk downward/toward the bottom
往前開	drive forward
往後退	withdraw backward

1. 從你家到學校，怎麼走？

_____

2. 從這兒到紐約(Niǔyuē 'New York')，怎麼走？

_____

3. 如果我想把車停(tíng 'to park')在路邊，我應該怎麼開？

_____

2. A 管 B 叫 X

A 管 B 叫 X	A calls B (as) X

1. 中國人管整天愛跳舞的人叫什麼？

_____

2. 中文管 World Wide Web 叫什麼？

_____

3. 美國人管什麼人叫 nerd？

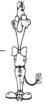

_____

3. The usage of 幫(忙)

A (AuxV) 幫 B VO	A helps B to VO
A (AuxV) 來/去幫忙	A (AuxV) come/go to help
A (AuxV) 幫 B 的忙	A helps B out

1. 我明天不能去上課，你能不能幫我跟老師請假？

_____

2. 如果你搬家的話，要請誰來幫忙？

_____

3. 你要我幫你什麼忙？

_____

4. The usage of 夠

S 夠了	S is enough
S (不)夠	S is not enough
X 夠 Adj 了	X is Adj enough
夠 No. M N V 了	to have enough amount/space for No. of N to V

You are planning a birthday party for your friend and you have invited six people. See if you have enough stuff.

1. 半打啤酒夠不夠？

_____

2. 三瓶汽水兒夠六個人喝嗎？

_____

3. 這個蛋糕 (dàn'gāo 'cake') 六個人吃夠不夠？

_____

5. The usage of SV 得很

S SV 得很	S is very Adj

1. 在中國，新年熱鬧不熱鬧啊？

_____

2. 放寒假的時候，你上哪兒去了？那兒好玩嗎？

_____

3. 你覺得這個學校的學生怎麼樣？

_____

C Reentry 複習 fùxí

1. 把…給… construction

S (AuxV/Neg) 把 O 給 V complement 了	S (AuxV/Neg) do/did … to O

1. 誰把我的書給拿下來了？

_____

 2. 那隻狗做了什麼「好事」？

_____

3. 他做了什麼了？

_____

 IV. Listening

1. Which one is true?
   a. Xiao Wang's address is 418 College Road.
   b. Xiao Wang's address is 178 College Road.
   c. Xiao Wang's address is 478 College Road.

2. How can we get to Xiao Wang's place?
   a. Go through the stoplight on Third Street and make a right on Rogers.
   b. Go past Rogers and turn right on Third Street.
   c. Make a right on Rogers and stop at Third Street.

3. Where is the college bookstore?
   a. On Third Street.
   b. On Fifth Street.
   c. On Second Street.
   d. On Sixth Street.

4. Going to the college bookstore you must pass…
   a. 2 traffic lights.
   b. 1 traffic light.
   c. 3 traffic lights.
   d. 0 traffic lights.

5. Why does A congratulate B?
   a. B just moved to a new apartment.
   b. B just moved to a dormitory.
   c. B just moved to an old house.
   d. B just moved to a new house.

6. How is B's new place?
   a. It's much bigger than their old one, but much less convenient for going to the mall.
   b. It's just a little bigger than their old one, and much more convenient for going to the mall.
   c. It's about the same size as their old one, but much less convenient for going to the mall.
   d. It's smaller than their old one, and much more convenient for going to the mall.

 V. Speaking

A. Talk about yourself
   Use the following questions as cues.
   1. 你家在哪兒？從學校到你家怎麼走？

   2. 現在這個地方你住了多久？你住得習慣嗎？地方大不大？

   3. 你什麼時候會請朋友到你家玩兒？你去看朋友的時候，會帶什麼東西去？

   4. 要是你的朋友搬了新家，你會送他東西嗎？你要送他什麼東西？

B. Good or Bad
   Talk to your classmates about good or bad accommodations you have had. Mention five aspects of life in a country/city that you could or could not get used to.

C. Interview a student from China or Taiwan and ask him/her how people celebrate Chinese New Year.

D. Talk about cultural differences
   Find a classmate who has a different cultural background and discuss the following:
   1. What kind of gathering/party is popular among students? What do they do when they party?
   2. Is dieting popular? What do people do to lose weight?
   3. Do people like to keep pets (chǒngwù 'pet')? Why do they keep pets? What kinds of pets do they have?

 VI. Reading

A. Read the Text
   Check your comprehension of the lesson dialogue by deciding whether the statements are true or false.

T / F　1.　Lín Měiyīng, Wáng Huá zhù zài Dàxuélù sān'èrjiǔ hào.　林美英、王華住在大學路、三二九號。

T / F　2.　Gāo Dézhōng dài .le qìshuǐr, yīn.wèi tā zhī.dào Měiyīng, Wáng Huá zài jiǎnféi.　高德中帶了汽水兒，因為他知道美英、王華在減肥。

T / F　3.　Lǐ Míng shuō Wáng Huá xǐ.huān tiàowǔ, suǒ.yǐ gēn Měiyīng yíkuàir qù duàn.liàn.　李明說王華喜歡跳舞 'dance,' 所以跟美英一塊兒去鍛練。

T / F　4.　Gāo Dézhōng shuō Měiyīng zhù .de dì.fāng hěn róng.yì zhǎo.　高德中說美英住的地方很容易找。

T / F　5.　Lín Měiyīng zhǎo Gāo Dézhōng, Lǐ Míng lái qìngzhù Zhōng.guó xīnnián.　林美英找高德中、李明來慶祝中國新年。

T / F　6.　Gāo Dézhōng xiǎng zhī.dào Zhōng.guó xīnnián zěn.me guò, suǒ.yǐ tā huì qù bāng Zhōng.guó tóngxuéhuì .de máng.　高德中想知道中國新年怎麼過，所以他會去幫中國同學會的忙。

T / F   7. Lín Měiyīng shuō tā.men .de wū.zi
hěn dà, zhù .le liù .ge rén.

林美英說她們的屋子很大，住了六個人。

T / F   8. Lǐ Míng jué.de Měiyīng, Wáng Huá
hěn yǒu yì.si, yīn.wèi tā.men yǎng .le
yú hé māo.

李明覺得美英、王華很有意思，因爲她們養了魚和貓。

T / F   9. Lín Měiyīng, Wáng Huá guǎn tā.men .de
māo jiào "wáng zǐ," yīn.wèi māo
hǎo.xiàng "Wáng Huá .de hái.zi."

林美英、王華管她們的貓叫「王子」，因爲貓好像「王華的孩子」。

B. Read the Authentic Material
1. Read the story on the right and
answer the questions.

a. What occasion did the author
celebrate?

_____

b. How did the author celebrate?

_____
_____
_____

c. What did they eat or drink on
this occasion?

_____

生日

丁 琳

上個星期六是我的好朋友小明的生日。他請了我們同班的同學到他家去慶祝他的生日。他媽媽和姐姐做了一個大蛋糕和很多餅乾，也準備了很多可口可樂和果汁。他爸爸還給我們每一個人一頂紙帽子和汽球。我們玩了很多遊戲。大家玩得滿身大汗，可是玩得很開心。今年我的生日，我也要請同學們來玩。

2. Read the story below and on the next page and answer the questions.

a. When did the author's family move? _____

b. How many stories does the new house have? _____ How many bedrooms and
TVs? _____

搬家

李 青

我們剛到加州的時候，因爲家裏沒有錢買房子，所以我們在公寓住了五年。後來因爲我們姐弟都長大了，爸媽覺得公寓太小了，應該搬家了。

今年一月爸爸媽媽就買了一個房子。放春假的時候，我們就搬家了。我們的新房子比公寓大多了。房子的前面和後面都有院子。樓上有四個臥房，兩間浴室。樓下有客廳，起居室，廚房，一間浴室和一個車庫。爸媽的臥房裏有一個電視機。起居室也有一個電視機。車庫可以停兩部車。前面的院子種了很多花和樹。後面的院子，除了種花以外，媽媽還開闢了一個小菜園，種了一些中國青菜。搬了家以後，我們姐弟三人在週末的時候也會幫媽媽拔野草和澆水，...

VII. Writing

A. Translate the following sentences into English and unscramble them into a coherent passage.

1. 晚會是六點開始(kāishǐ 'to start') 的。

   _____

2. 我不知道自己吃了多少東西，但是吃完的時候，我的肚子好像個球似的，都走不動了。

   _____

3. 聽說除了學生以外，這裏很多的中國老師也來幫忙。

   _____

4. 那個晚會一共有兩百多人參加，很熱鬧也很有意思。

   _____

5. 上星期五晚上我去參加(cānjiā 'to attend') 一個新年晚會，是中國同學會辦的。

   _____

6. 大家先吃飯再看表演 (biǎoyǎn 'performance')。

   _____

7. The correct order for a coherent passage is: _____

8. Write one or two sentences to complete the passage.

_____

_____

B. Read the letter from your parents below. Write an answer to it.

How do you like the place you just moved into? Is it big? Is it quiet? Is it safe (安全 ānquán)? Is it convenient to get to school and go shopping? Can you get used to life off campus? Do you cook for yourself? Do you invite friends over for dinner? Do you fight (吵架 chǎojià) with your roommate?

親愛的爸爸媽媽：
我現在住的地方很好。

第十七課 你洗好澡了沒有？

 I. Vocabulary

A. Explain the meaning of the following words in Chinese.

1. húshuō　　胡說　_____

2. áoyè　　熬夜　_____

3. màntūntūn　慢吞吞　_____

4. dǎoméi　倒霉　_____

5. hàodòng　好動　_____

B. Make a sentence that incorporates a word suggested by the picture.

1. _____ 　　　3. _____

2. _____ 　　　4. _____

C. Choose the appropriate word to complete the following sentences.

1. Kuài yì.diǎnr xiě, zhǐ (gòu, shèng, dāi) shí
   fēnzhōng .le.

   快一點兒寫，只（夠、剩、待）十分
   鐘了。

2. Nǐ gēn tā, yí .ge wàixiàng yí .ge nèixiàng,
   zhènghǎo (hé, gǎn, pèi) chéng yí duìr.

   你跟他，一個外向一個內向，正好
   （合、趕、配）成一對兒。

3. Nà .ge hái.zi xǐ.huān (yìzhí cuī, húshuō,
   jí.sǐ rén), bié tīng tā .de.

   那個孩子喜歡（一直催、胡說、急死
   人），別聽他的。

4. (Wǎn.le, Suàn.le, Zāo.le), wǒ méi dài
   xiànjīn, zěn.me fù qián .ne!

   （晚了、算了、糟了），我沒帶現金，
   怎麼付錢呢！

II. Characters   **Worksheet 28**

Hàn zì	直	等	急	害	晚	慢	當	然	雖	更
Notes	zhí straight 8	děng to wait 12	jí nervous 9	hài to injure 10	wǎn evening 11	màn slow 14	dāng ought 13	rán thus, so 12	suí, suī although 17	gèng even more 7
1										
2										
3										
4										
5										
6										

	Compound/Phrase/Sentence/Journal/Memory Aid
直	
等	
急	
害	
晚	
慢	
當	
然	
雖	
更	

Hàn zì	内	向	洗	澡	睡	覺	臉	定	意	思
Notes	nèi inner 4	xiàng to turn 6	xǐ to wash 9	zǎo to bathe 16	shuì to sleep 13	jiào perceive 20	liǎn face 17	dìng to decide 8	yì thought 13	sī to think 9
1										
2										
3										
4										
5										
6										

	Compound/Phrase/Sentence/Journal/Memory Aid
内	
向	
洗	
澡	
睡	
覺	
臉	
定	
意	
思	

III. Grammar

A Major Sentence Patterns

1. 什麼都..., 就是... **construction**

| S 什麼(N)都...就是... | S can do everything (Adv) except... |

1. 你的老師好不好？

   _____

2. 這兒你什麼地方都去過嗎？

   _____

3. 你的貓(or other pet/object)怎麼樣？

   _____

2. 可..., 要不然... **construction**

| S 可(不/別) VO , 要不然 (S)... | S by all/no means do VO; otherwise (S) will... |

Advise me not to do the following.

1. 我天天熬夜。

   _____

2. 我一天喝六杯咖啡。

   _____

3. 我想去燙髮。

   _____

3. The conditional usage of 才

| S ... , (S) 才 VO | Only if S... then (S) will VO |

1. 老師說你得做什麼才能把中文學好？

   _____

2. 現在你得做什麼才有精神念書？

_____

3. 你把車練好了，才能怎麼樣？

_____

4. A 對 B 有意思／有興趣

A 對 B (person/thing) (Adv) 有意思／有興趣	A is (Adv) interested in B
A 對 B (person/thing)　　沒有意思／沒有興趣	A is not interested in B
A 對 B (person/thing) 一點兒意思／興趣都／也沒有	A has no interest in B at all

1. 你覺得小高對小林有沒有意思？

_____

2. 在 _____ (name of a movie that's about a love story) 電影裏誰對誰有意思？

_____

3. 你對什麼有興趣？

_____

4. 你對中國電影有沒有興趣？為什麼？

_____

B Usage of Common Phrases

1. The adverbial phrase 快／慢一點兒

快／慢 一點兒!	Hurry up!/Slow down!
快／慢 一點兒 V!	V a little faster/slower!
(VO) V 快／慢 一點兒	does (O) a little faster/slower

Make a request to do the following.

1. To avoid being late for a class.

_____

2. To avoid a speeding ticket.

_____

3. To make sure you understand what the teacher said.

_____

2. The causative markers 害、弄

| S 害 (得) O V... | S causes/caused O to V... |
| S 弄 (得) O V... | S makes/made   O to V... |

1. 他把你的電腦弄壞了，害得你怎麼了？

_____

2. 樓上的房客一直吵，弄得你怎麼了？

_____

3. 她開車開得太慢，害得你怎麼了？

_____

ⓒ Reentry

1. 為什麼 and 因為 ..., 所以...

| S 為什麼 (AuxV/Neg) V O (呢)? (MA) | Why is it that S (not) V O? |
| 因為 S..., 所以 (S)... | Because S..., therefore S... |

1. 你為什麼今天又遲到了？

_____

2. 你為什麼昨天沒交功課？

_____

3. 為什麼你一直催我去剪頭髮？

_____

IV. Listening

1. Which one is true?
   a. Xiao Wang wants to take a shower.
   b. Xiao Wang wants to blow dry her hair.
   c. Xiao Wang wants to wash her face.

2. Which one is true?
   a. Xiao Lin doesn't have to attend class; she will let Xiao Wang use the bathroom first.
   b. Xiao Lin has to attend class, but she will let Xiao Wang use the bathroom first.
   c. Xiao Lin has to attend class; she doesn't want to let Xiao Wang use the bathroom first.

3. What did A suggest that B do?
   a. A suggested that B get up early tomorrow.
   b. A suggested that B go to bed early tonight.
   c. A suggested that B write the paper tomorrow.
   d. A suggested that B burn midnight oil to write the paper tonight.

4. What kind of person is Xiao Chen?
   a. Xiao Chen is honest and introverted.
   b. Xiao Chen is active and outgoing.
   c. Xiao Chen is quiet and considerate.
   d. Xiao Chen is very aggressive.

5. Ding doesn't like Xiao Chen because:
   a. Xiao Chen is implulsive.
   b. Xiao Chen is not active and outgoing.
   c. Xiao Chen is not handsome.
   d. Xiao Chen is not open-minded.

 V. Speaking

A. Talk about yourself
   Use the following questions as cues.
   1. 你跟別人一塊兒住過沒有？(Have you ever shared a room or an apartment?)
      跟別人一塊兒住麻煩不麻煩？為什麼？

   2. 你的同屋是個怎麼樣的人？你喜歡他/她嗎？

3. 你喜歡跟什麼樣的人做朋友？

4. 你是不是個夜貓子？你平常什麼時候洗澡、睡覺？為什麼？

B. Opinion Poll
Interview your classmates to find out their reactions to the following questions.
1. 你覺得早睡早起好還是晚睡晚起好？為什麼？
2. 你覺得早上洗澡好還是晚上洗澡好？為什麼？
3. 你覺得長頭髮好看還是短頭髮好看？為什麼？
4. 你覺得跟內向的人做朋友好還是跟外向的人做朋友好？為什麼？

C. Show and Tell
Bring to class a couple of pictures of your family/relatives/friends or those of movie stars and celebrities. Display them in front of the class and have your classmates point out the persons as you describe them.   Mention their outfits, appearance, and temperament.

D. Find Mr./Miss Right
Someone wants to date your best friend. What questions would you ask to find out more about his/her personality, appearance, interests, etc.?

 VI. Reading

A. Read the Text
Check your comprehension of the lesson dialogue by answering the following questions.

1. Wáng Huá píngcháng zuòshì màntūntūn .de, wèishén.me jīn.tiān zǎo.shàng zhè.me jí?   王華平常做事慢吞吞的，為什麼今天早上這麼急？

_____

2. Wèishén.me Měiyīng yào zǎo.shàng xǐzǎo?   為什麼美英要早上洗澡？

_____

3. Wáng Huá wèishén.me shuō zìjǐ "zhēn dǎoméi?"   王華為什麼說自己「真倒霉」？

_____

4.   Lín Měiyīng yào Wáng Huá yíhòu bié zài zuò shén.me? Wèishén.me tā zhè.me shuō?   林美英要王華以後別再做什麼？為什麼她這麼說？

_____

5.   Wáng Huá gēn Měiyīng zài shēnghuó shàng yǒu shén.me bù yíyàng?   王華跟美英在生活上有什麼不一樣？

_____

6.   Wáng Huá wèishén.me shuō Měiyīng yīnggāi bǎ tóu.fà jiǎnduǎn?   王華為什麼說美英應該把頭髮剪短？

_____

7.   Lín Měiyīng zen3.me shuo1 zi4ji3 dui4 Gao1 De2zhong1 "mei3.you3 yi4.si?"   林美英怎麼說自己對高德中「沒有意思」？

_____

8.   Wei4shen2.me Wáng Huá shuo1 Mei3ying1 gen1 Gao1 De2zhong1 shi4 "yi2 dui4r?"   為什麼王華說美英跟高德中是「一對兒」？

_____

9.   Měiyīng shuo1 Wáng Huá gen1 shei2 shi4 "yi2 dui4r?" Wèishén.me?   美英說王華跟誰是「一對兒」？為什麼？

_____

B. Read the Authentic Material
   1. Read the advertisement and choose correct answer(s).
     _____ a. The person who posted this ad was (1) 45 (2) 25 (3) 44 years old.

     _____ b. This person loves (1) music (2) exercise (3) fair ladies.

     _____ c. This person (1) has blue eyes (2) is from China (3) is looking for a pen pal.

   2. Read the following ad and decide whether the statement is true or false.
     T F a. The person who posted this ad is from China but knows English.

     T F b. This person is looking for someone who practices medicine.

     T F c. This person is 54 years old and looking for a companion under 65 years old.

徵男婚友

大陸女醫生54高1.66米
知書達理溫文善良精
醫技懂英語覓65以下
誠實有職男公民為伴
請洽：
1520 Fountain Drive
Los Angeles, CA 45020
513-450-4837

VII. Writing

A. Translate the following into English, reorder them into a coherent passage, and write a title.

1. 如果他不喜歡你，也一定會讓你知道的。

   _____

2. 他這樣東搬搬、西弄弄，每天都忙得很。

   _____

3. 他平常對什麼都有興趣，總是(zǒngshì 'always')在屋子裏走來走去，把東西從一個地方搬到另外一個地方，一點兒也不覺得麻煩。

   _____

4. 老王真有意思，每天一早就起床，很晚才睡覺。

   _____

5. 老王除了好動、外向以外，也很老實。

   _____

6. 他什麼都好，就是脾氣有一點兒急，頭髮有一點兒長，而且他不喜歡洗澡。

   _____

7. 雖然這樣，他對人還是很好的，所以他的朋友很多。

   _____

8. 他一看見朋友來了，就高興 (gāoxìng 'happy') 得大喊大叫。

   _____

9. The correct order for a coherent passage is: _____

10. A title for this passage might be: _____

11. Can you draw a portrait of 老王？

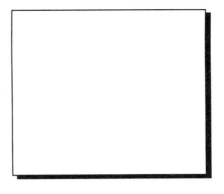

B. Leave a note for your roommate on the refrigerator. Remind her/him not to stay up too late tonight. S/he has already been late for Chinese class twice and needs to get up early tomorrow morning. Remind your roommate of the teacher's temperament and the course requirement regarding the late policy. Use the patterns:
1. S 什麼(N) 都 …, 就 是 …
2. 可別 …, 要不然 …
3. S…才 … (conditional usage)
4. 因爲 …, 所 以 …

第十八課 你聽過中國音樂嗎？

I. Vocabulary

A. Write the antonym of the following words in pinyin and English.

1. chuántǒng   傳統   ↔   _____   _____
2. wàiháng   外行   ↔   _____   _____
3. dōngfāng   東方   ↔   _____   _____
4. jǐn.zhāng   緊張   ↔   _____   _____
5. wàng .le   忘了   ↔   _____   _____

B. Explain the meaning of the following words in Chinese.

1. yīnmáng   音盲   _____
2. yuèduì   樂隊   _____
3. duànkǎo   段考   _____
4. yǒu yánjiū   有研究 _____
5. wàiháng   外行   _____

C. Choose the appropriate word/phrase to complete the following sentences/dialogue.

1. Nǐ děi (hǎohāor, hǎoxiàng, shízú) .de
    duàn.liàn, yào.bùrán shēntǐ huì bù hǎo.

    你得(好好兒 、好像 、十足)地鍛練
    ，要不然身體會不好。

2. A: Nǐ búbì mǎi dōng.xī gěi hái.zi.
    B: (Bié dānxīn, Bié kè.qì, Bié shuō .le).

    A: 你不必買東西給孩子。
    B: (別擔心 、別客氣 、別說了)。

3. Tā shàngkè .de shí.hòu bù (lǎo.shí, qíguài,
    zhuānxīn), suǒ.yǐ méi tīng.jiàn lǎoshī shuō
    .de.

    他上課的時候不(老實 、奇怪 、專心)
    ，所以沒聽見老師說的。

4. Wǒ.men zhè .ge zhōumò (biàn, zǔ, jù)
    yíxià, chī .ge fàn zěn.meyàng?

    我們這個週末(變 、組、聚)一下，吃
    個飯怎麼樣？

II. Characters   **Worksheet 30**

Hàn zì	考	唱	新	歌	研	究	音	樂	客	氣
Notes	kǎo to test 6	chàng to sing 11	xīn new 13	gē to sing 14	yán to study 9	jiū to study carefully 7	yīn sound 9	yuè music 15	kè guest 9	qì air 10
1										
2										
3										
4										
5										
6										

	Compound/Phrase/Sentence/Journal/Memory Aid
考	
唱	
新	
歌	
研	
究	
音	
樂	
客	
氣	

Worksheet 31

Hàn zì	漂	亮	忘	記	專	心	尤	其	實	連
Notes	piào pretty 14	liàng bright 9	wàng to forget 7	jì to remember 10	zhuān focused 11	xīn heart 4	yóu especially 4	qí his, her 8	shí solid 14	lián to connect 11
1										
2										
3										
4										
5										
6										

	Compound/Phrase/Sentence/Journal/Memory Aid
漂	
亮	
忘	
記	
專	
心	
尤	
其	
實	
連	

SVO

III. Grammar

A Major Sentence Patterns

1. 連...都... construction

連　S　　　　　　　都 V (了)	Even S...
S　連　O(generic N)　都 V (了)	S even V...
S　連一 M N　都/也　不/沒 V	S doesn't even V...

1. 什麼人都喝可口可樂(kěkǒu kělè 'coke') 嗎？

   對了，連中國人_____

2. 你什麼音樂都聽嗎？(including rock-and-roll)

   _____

3. 你會說韓文(Hánwén 'Korean') 嗎？

   _____

2. A 對 B 有研究

A 對 B　　　　有研究	A has done research/study on B
A 對 B　　沒有研究	A hasn't done research/study on B
A 對 B 一點兒研究 都/也 沒有	A hasn't done any research/study on B at all
A 對 B 沒什麼研究	A hasn't done much research/study on B

1. 你對什麼有研究？

   _____

2. 你對京劇有研究沒有？

   _____

3. 誰對美國的音樂很有研究？

   _____

3. A 給 B 寄 O 來/去

A (Neg) 給 B 寄 O 來/去	A (Neg) sends O to B (here/there)
A (Neg) 給 B 寄 來/去 O	

1. 耶誕節的時候，你父母給你寄了什麼東西來？

_____

2. 過年的時候，誰給你寄東西來？

_____

3. 你朋友生日的時候，你給她寄去了什麼東西？

_____

4. More resultative verb compounds

Actual form	V RE	do V
Positive potential form	V得RE	be able to V
Negative potential form	V不 RE	not be able to V

1. 那本中文書他看得懂嗎？

_____

2. 同學說得很小聲，你聽得見聽不見？

_____

3. 老師說得很快，你聽得懂聽不懂？

_____

4. 《喜福會》那本小說你一天看得完看不完？

_____

5. 一個pizza你一個人吃得下吃不下？

_____

6. 那個屋子一個月六百五，你住得起嗎？

_____

7. 你漢字的功課三十分鐘寫得好嗎？

_____

8. 喝了咖啡以後，你睡得著睡不著？

_____

9. 現在走，紐約(Niǔyuē 'New York') 你明天到得了到不了？

_____

B Usage of Common Phrases

1. Vivid reduplicates

| A Ā 兒地 |

1. 他去過中國，在中國住了五年。 (Then let's ask him to talk about his life in China.)

_____

2. 他兩天沒睡，累死了。 (He needs to have a good rest.)

_____

3. 我明天有中文的段考。 (You need to prepare well tonight.)

_____

 IV. Listening

1. Which one is true?
   a. Xiao Lin can sing many Chinese folk songs.
   b. Xiao Lin can sing one Chinese folk song, but has forgotten the lyrics to it.
   c. Xiao Lin cannot sing any Chinese folk songs at all.

2. Which one is true?
   a. Xiao Wang knows a lot about Beijing opera.
   b. Xiao Wang doesn't know anything about Beijing opera.
   c. Xiao Wang has studied Beijing opera, but can't sing very well.

3. How is Xiao Gao's Chinese?
   a. His grammar and tones are both very good.
   b. His grammar is very good, but he still has problems with tones.
   c. Both his grammar and tones are still not very good.
   d. His grammar is very bad, but his tones are very good.

4. Has Xiao Gao learned any Chinese songs?
    a. He has never studied how to sing Chinese songs.
    b. He has learned many Chinese songs.
    c. He has studied only two songs.
    d. He has learned only one song.

5. Has B ever seen Beijing opera?
    a. B has seen Beijing opera many times.
    b. B has never seen Beijing opera.
    c. B has seen Beijing opera seven times.
    d. B has seen Beijing opera only one time.

6. How well can B play the Chinese "húqínr"?
    a. B cannot play the Chinese "húqínr"at all.
    b. B has studied how to play the "húqín" for a long time, but still can't play very well.
    c. B has studied for just one month, but plays it very well.
    d. B has studied for only one month, and still can't play it very well.

 # V. Speaking

A. Talk about yourself
    Use the following questions as cues.
    1. 你聽過中國音樂嗎？聽過什麼樣的音樂？

    2. 你喜歡聽民歌、爵士樂、搖滾樂還是別的流行歌曲？

    3. 你最喜歡哪個樂隊？你喜歡聽誰唱的歌兒？爲什麼？

    4. 你自己喜歡唱歌嗎？你會玩什麼樂器(yuèqì 'musical instrument')？你 X 拉、彈 (lā/tán 'to play') 得怎麼樣？

    5. 你考完試的時候，都做些什麼讓自己輕鬆一下？

B. Best Hit

Survey your classmates to find out their favorite song from the 1960s, '70s or '80s and what the lyrics are about.

Song	Name	Year	About
1.			
2.			
3.			
4.			
5.			

C. Cultural differences

1. Talk to a Chinese friend to find out what Beijing operas are like.
2. Talk to a classmate of another cultural background and have him/her teach you a song.
3. Work with a partner to compare Chinese music with another country's music that you know. Discuss whether Chinese music has been influenced by that of other countries.

 VI. Reading

A. Read the Text

Check your comprehension of the lesson dialogue by deciding whether the statements are true or false.

T / F 1. Gāo Dézhōng bú rèn.de (to recognize) Měiyīng, yīn.wèi hǎo jiǔ méi kàn.dào tā .le.　　高德中不認得美英，因爲好久沒看到她了。

T / F 2. Gāo Dézhōng jué.de Měiyīng .de yàng.zi biàn .le hěn duō, gèng piào.liàng .le.　　高德中覺得美英的樣子變了很多，更漂亮了。

T / F 3. Měiyīng zài tīng CD, suǒ.yǐ méi tīng.jiàn Gāo Dézhōng jiào tā.　　美英在聽CD，所以沒聽見高德中叫她。

T / F 4. Měiyīng .de dì.dì jì .le "Zhōng.guó shì .de juéshìyuè" gěi tā tīng.　　美英的弟弟寄了「中國式的爵士樂」給她聽。

T / F 5. Měiyīng jué.de Zhōng.guó xiàndài yīnyuè shòu .le Xīfāng hěn dà .de yǐngxiǎng.　　美英覺得中國現代音樂受了西方很大的影響。

T / F   6. Gāo Dézhōng duì Zhōng.guó yīnyuè hěn nèiháng, tīng.guò hěn duō chuántǒng .de mín'gē.

高德中對中國音樂很內行，聽過很多傳統的民歌。

T / F   7. Lín Měiyīng xiàn.zài hái huì chàng "Mòlìhuā," yīn.wèi xiǎoshí.hòu xué.guò.

林美英現在還會唱「茉莉花」，因為小時候學過。

T / F   8. Lín Měiyīng jué.de zìjǐ bú tài dǒng Zhōng.guó yīnyuè.

林美英覺得自己不太懂中國音樂。

T / F   9. Wáng Huá hé Lǐ Míng dōu duì jīngjù hěn yǒu yánjiū.

王華和李明都對京劇很有研究。

B. Read the Authentic Material

1. Read the journal[1] below and choose the correct answer(s).

a. _____ This journal was written on (1) October 12 (2) November 15 (3) October 15.

b. _____ The author liked the place she visited because (1) it had many jasmine flowers (2) it was in a beautiful suburban area (3) it had fresh air.

c. _____ The author (1) shared her visit with her classmates (2) learned how to sing "Jasmine Flowers" (3) visited the place twice.

我的日記

十月十五日　星期二　晴

今天，媽媽說這個星期六要帶我們到外婆家去，我好高興。

記得暑假的時候，媽媽帶我們到外婆家住了好幾天，那是我最快樂的日子。我把好多有趣的事記下來了，開學以後，還說給同學們聽呢。

外婆的家在鄉下。每次媽媽帶我們到外婆家，外婆都說：「我們鄉下空氣好，青菜多，花兒香，多住幾天吧！」

我最喜歡外婆院子裡的茉莉花。表姊教我畫茉莉花，又教我唱「茉莉花」的歌，我很快就學會了。這個歌真好聽啊！

[1] This is from 國民小學二年級上學期國語課本. By 國立編譯館, 台北, 1996.

2. Read the following story and answer the questions.

a. What kind of show is the author writing about?_____

b. Is the show interesting? Why? _____

_____

c. What does the author think about the performers' costumes?

_____

京劇

王小平

　　幾年以前我們都沒看過京劇。爸媽常說我們看不懂，所以都不帶我們去看。最近幾年，電視臺也播放京劇節目。因為電視上的京劇有漢字字幕，所以我們就看得懂了。京劇裏的演員很有意思。他們的臉，有的是紅色的，有的是白色的，有的是黑色的，還有的是藍色的。他們穿的衣服和鞋子也很好玩兒，很奇怪。他們演的時候更有意思，他們很少說話，大部份是唱的，很像美國的歌劇。其實他們唱歌還是說話都很難懂，不過我覺得沒看過的人都應該看一看。

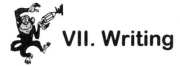

VII. Writing

A. Recall a song from your childhood and see if you can translate its lyrics into Chinese to help teach your Chinese friend the song.

English: ....

Chinese: ....

English: ....

Chinese: ....

English: ....

Chinese: ....

English: ....

Chinese: ....

English: ....

Chinese: ....

B. Read the want ad on the left and respond by filling in the blanks with the missing word or words.

Tutor wanted to teach guitar on weekends.

$160/mo.

Call Jan Lee —
      356-2121 or
      356-4500

李太太

您好！

我對音樂很有＿＿＿＿1，對教人學音樂也很有＿＿＿＿2。我在印大＿＿＿＿3小提琴，副修吉他。大學生、中學生我都＿＿＿＿4，＿＿＿＿5小學生我也教過。我可以來你家教，也可以在學校教。週末下午我多半兒都＿＿＿＿6。學費我們可以見了再說。我的＿＿＿＿7是三四六・六三八三。

第十九課 哪一隊贏了？

I. Vocabulary

A. Look at the following picture and fill in the appropriate new words in pinyin.

B. Explain the meaning of the following words in Chinese.

1. bùrú　　　　不如　＿＿＿＿＿＿＿＿＿＿＿＿＿＿＿＿＿＿＿
2. píngshǒu　　平手　＿＿＿＿＿＿＿＿＿＿＿＿＿＿＿＿＿＿＿
3. fànguī　　　犯規　＿＿＿＿＿＿＿＿＿＿＿＿＿＿＿＿＿＿＿
4. hǎoqiú　　　好球　＿＿＿＿＿＿＿＿＿＿＿＿＿＿＿＿＿＿＿

C. Choose one from the parentheses that paraphrases the italicized word in the sentence.

1. Tā fāqiú fā .de hěn lì.hài, bù róng.yì dǎ.dào. (bùxíng, hěn lèirén, hǎojí.le)

   他發球發得很厲害，不容易打到。
   (不行、很累人、好極了)

2. Shàng bàn chǎng Mìxīgēn duì lǐngxiān. (dǎ .de bǐjiào hǎo, xiān fāqiú, bù rú wǒ.men)

   上半場密西根隊領先。
   (打得比較好、先發球、不如我們)

3. Ai.yā! Wǒ bù xíng .le, lèi.sǐ .le. (yǐ.jīng bù hǎo .le, bù néng zài dǎ .le, zǎo jiù yào zǒu .le)

   哎呀！我不行了，累死了。
   (已經不好了、不能再打了、早就要走了)

4. Nà .ge cáipàn yí kàn bú duì, jiù jiào zhàntíng. (xiē shí fēnzhōng, tíng bàntiān, tíng yì huǐr)

   那個裁判一看不對，就叫暫停。
   (歇十分鐘、停半天、停一會兒)

II. Characters

Hàn zì	隊	員	手	視	昨	夜	輸	贏	教	練
Notes	duì team 12	yuán a person 10	shǒu hand 4	shì to look at 11	zuó yesterday 9	yè night 8	shū to lose 16	yíng to win 20	jiāo to teach 11	liàn practice 15
1										
2										
3										
4										
5										
6										

	Compound/Phrase/Sentence/Journal/Memory Aid
隊	
員	
手	
視	
昨	
夜	
輸	
贏	
教	
練	

Hàn zì	停	賽	難	拉	變	低	應	該	必	發
Notes	tíng stop 11	sài to compete 17	nán difficult 19	lā to pull 8	biàn to change 23	dī low 7	yīng should 17	gāi should 13	bì must 5	fā to rise 12
1										
2										
3										
4										
5										
6										

	Compound/Phrase/Sentence/Journal/Memory Aid
停	
賽	
難	
拉	
變	
低	
應	
該	
必	
發	

SVO

III. Grammar

Ⓐ Major Sentence Patterns

1. 再過..., 就 ... **construction**

(S) 再過 多久 就 ... 呢？ 再過 多久 (S) 就 ... 呢？	In how long will (S) be...?
(S) 再過 Time Expression 就 ... 再過 Time Expression (S) 就 ...	In another Time Expression, (S) will be...

1. 我們再過多久就要放春假了呢？

_____

2. 再過多久你的朋友就會來看你呢？

_____

3. 你再過多久就要上中國去呢？

_____

2. Comparison of two events

V_1O_1 比 V_2O_2 還/更 Adj V_1 O_1 沒(有)V_2 O_2 (那麼/這麼) Adj	To do V_1O_1 is even Adj-er than V_2O_2 To do V_1O_1 is not as Adj as V_2O_2

1. 日文很難。你覺得學中文比學日文還難嗎？

_____

2. 看人打球很累。自己打球比看人打球還累嗎？

_____

3. 打網球很有意思。你覺得打籃球比打網球更有意思嗎？

_____

3. Comparison of two performances

3.1 比 comparison

A　VO V得 比 B (更/還) Adj O, A　V得 比 B (更/還) Adj	A　VO Adj-er than B As for O, A　V Adj-er than B
A　VO V得 沒(有) B (那麼/這麼) Adj O, A　V得 沒(有) B (那麼/這麼) Adj	A　doesn't VO　as Adj as　B As for O, A doesn't V as Adj as B

Compare 張、王 on the following activities, e.g., 小王看電視看得跟小張一樣多嗎？不，電視小王看得沒有小張那麼多。

Activity	小王	小張
打籃球	進八球	進五球
打網球	得五分	得五分
看電視	一天兩小時	一天三小時
看電影	一個月一次	一個月兩次

1. _____

_____

2. _____

_____

3. _____

_____

3.2　Equal comparison

A　VO　V得跟　　B 一樣　Adj	A　VO　as Adj as　B does
A　VO　V得不跟 B 一樣　Adj	A doesn't VO equally Adj with　B
A　VO　V得跟 B不一樣　Adj	A and B do not VO equally Adj
O,　A　V得跟　　B 一樣　Adj	As for O, A doesn't VO equally Adj with　B
O,　A　V得不跟 B 一樣　Adj	As for O, A　V as Adj as　B　does
O,　A　V得跟 B不一樣　Adj	As for O, A and B do not V equally Adj

1. 你覺得Michael Jackson 唱歌唱得好還是他妹妹唱歌唱得好？

_____

2. 你覺得Harrison Ford演戲演得好還是Tom Hanks演戲演得好？

_____

3. 小林打球打得好還是小王打球打得好？

_____

B Usage of Common Phrases

1. A 不如 B... construction

A 不如 B SV	A is not as Adj as B
V_1O_1 不如 V_2O_2	To do V_1O_1 is not as good as to do V_2O_2 It is better to do V_2O_2 than to do V_1O_1
一 M 不如 一 M	(It's) getting ...er M by M

1. 打籃球，中國隊不如美國隊厲害嗎？

_____

2. 打網球比打高爾夫球輕鬆嗎？

不，_____

3. 你桌球 'table tennis' 打得怎麼樣？

_____

4. 最近的天氣怎麼樣？(getting worse year by year)

真奇怪，_____

2. The co-verb 跟

A (AuxV) 跟 B VO	A (AuxV) VO with B
A (不/沒/別) 跟 B VO	A (not) VO with B

1. 最近哪個學校跟哪個學校比賽打籃球啊？

_____

2. 你會打乒乓球嗎？是跟誰學的啊？

_____

3. 誰跟誰在那兒練網球啊？

_____

3. Winning prizes and awards

A 得了冠軍	A dé.le guànjūn	A won the championship
A 得了亞軍	A dé.le yàjūn	A was the runner-up
A 得了季軍	A dé.le jìjūn	A was the second runner-up
A 得了金牌	A dé.le jīnpái	A won the gold medal
A 得了銀牌	A dé.le yínpái	A won the silver medal
A 得了銅牌	A dé.le tóngpái	A won the bronze medal
A 得了第一名	A dé.le dìyīmíng	A won first place
A 得了第二名	A dé.le dìèrmíng	A won second place
A 得了第三名	A dé.le dìsānmíng	A won third place

1. 你們學校的籃球隊怎麼樣？得過全國冠軍沒有？

   _____

2. Carl Louis 得過多少個金牌？

   _____

3. 你喜歡打乒乓球嗎？得過第一名沒有？

   _____

C Reentry

1. The difference between 跟、和、也

NP₁ 跟 NP₂	NP₁ and NP₂
NP₁ 和 NP₂	NP₁ and NP₂
VP₁ 也 VP₂	VP₁ and VP₂

1. 你就喜歡打網球嗎？

   不，_____

2. 這兒只有你喜歡聽搖滾樂嗎？

   不，_____

3. 你覺得自己在家做飯有意思嗎？

   _____

Fill in the following blanks with 跟、和 or 也

4. 日本人＿＿＿中國人都喜歡喝茶。

5. 這一隊打得很好，那一隊 ＿＿＿打得很好。

6. 我喜歡打網球＿＿＿喜歡打高爾夫球。

7. 他愛滑雪 ＿＿＿ 游泳。

8. 小王喜歡喝啤酒＿＿＿汽水。

9. 他們的公寓很大＿＿＿很舒服。

 IV. Listening

1. What kind of game is IU playing with Purdue?
   a. Volleyball.
   b. Soccer.
   c. Tennis.
   d. Basketball.

2. Which team won the game?
   a. Purdue won.
   b. IU won.
   c. Purdue and IU tied.
   d. The game was canceled.

3. Why doesn't Xiao Lin want to play tennis with Xiao Wang?
   a. Playing tennis is boring.
   b. Playing tennis is too tiring.
   c. Playing tennis is too easy.
   d. Playing tennis is too time consuming.

4. What do Xiao Lin and Xiao Wang decide to do?
   a. To ski.
   b. To play golf .
   c. To swim.
   d. To play basketball.

V. Speaking

A. Talk about yourself
   Use the following questions as cues.
   1. 你平常看球賽嗎？你喜歡看什麼球賽？爲什麼？

   2. 你平常打球嗎？你喜歡打什麼球？爲什麼？

   3. 你覺得看什麼球賽最沒有意思？爲什麼？

   4. 你覺得打什麼球最累人？爲什麼？

B. A Popular Program
   You are a journalist working on a report of popular TV programs this year.   Ask your
   classmates the following questions:
   1. Which TV program (節目 jiémù) (not limited to sports) does she/he like to watch?
   2. What is the program about?
   3. When and what channel (第幾台 dìjǐ tái) is the program on?
   4. Would she/he recommend the program to a young audience?

C. Rules of the Game
   Talk to sports fans in your class and have them briefly explain the rules for a basketball
   game.
   Here are some sample questions:
   1. 每一隊有幾個球員？
   2. 每一場可以打多少分鐘？
   3. 進一球可以得幾分？罰球最多可以得幾分？
   4. 怎麼樣是犯規？

VI. Reading

A. Read the Text
   Check your comprehension of the lesson dialogue by answering the following questions.
   1. Wèishén.me Wáng Huá yào Měiyīng bié　　爲什麼王華要美英別睡懶覺了？
       shuì lǎn jiào .le?

2. Měiyīng wèishén.me bù xiǎng qǐlái?   美英爲什麼不想起來？

    _____

3. Wáng Huá jué.de Mìxīgēn .de qiúduì dǎ .de   王華覺得密西根的球隊打得怎麼
    zěn.meyàng? Wèishén.me?   樣？爲什麼？

    _____

4. Wáng Huá jué.de cáipàn hǎo.bùhǎo?   王華覺得裁判好不好？爲什麼？
    Wèishén.me?

    _____

5. Lín Měiyīng yào Wáng Huá péi tā qù zuò   林美英要王華陪她去做什麼？她
    shén.me? Tā jué.de kàn rén dǎ qiú yǒuyì.si   覺得看人打球有意思嗎？
    .ma?

    _____

6. Wáng Huá .de wǎngqiú dǎ .de zěn.meyàng?   王華的網球打得怎麼樣？你怎麼
    Nǐ zěn.me zhī.dào?   知道？

    _____

7. Měiyīng zěn.me gǔlì Wáng Huá?   美英怎麼鼓勵王華？

    _____

8. Wáng Huá jué.de dǎ qiú hǎo hái.shì kàn qiú   王華覺得打球好還是看球好？你
    hǎo? Nǐ zěn.me zhī.dào?   怎麼知道？

    _____

9. Wáng Huá jué.de dǎ wǎngqiú yǒu shén.me   王華覺得打網球有什麼不好？下
    bù hǎo? Xià.cì yīnggāi zěn.me bàn (to do)?   次應該怎麼辦？

    _____

B. Read the Authentic Material
    1. Read the following advertisement and answer the questions.
        a. What kind of competition is this? _____

        b. How many schools and how many students participated in the competition?

            _____

        c. Where is the location of this competition?_____

世界日報　　　　　　　十六年三月二十五日　星期二

中文識字比賽

十一所中文學校　一百廿九名學生報名角逐

【本報芝加哥訊】由美中中文學校協會及華美芝北中文學校及大都會保險公司合辦的九七年美中地區中文學校中文識字比賽，二十二日在奧克頓學院舉行，九組的小朋友競爭比賽下共有五十四位小朋友獲得名次。

識字比賽是中文學校的大事，參與的小朋友共有一百二十九人，學校共有十一所，參加的小朋友都由家長陪同參加，有的家庭全家都到為孩子或孫子打氣，參加的約有五百人，會場尚有各種攤位介紹讓家長在小朋友考試時也有地方可去。

大都會保險公司自紐約來的副總裁兼亞裔部主任的張泰田表示，該公司已連續贊助識字比賽三年，主要是認為下一代中保持自己的文化與語言對亞裔移民及亞裔家庭是很重要的。具有雙語能力與多元化文化薰陶的亞裔新一代將在競爭的全球經濟中佔有一席之地，該公司是秉著取之社會回饋社區的理想對亞裔社區，特別是對華人社區的文化與公益事業支持不遺餘力，贊助芝加哥地區中文學校識字比賽是參與亞裔社區文化活動計畫的一部分。

中文學校協會會長葉少基感謝大都會的贊助且對十一個中文學校的組織和策劃合作精神特別誇讚，僑教中心主任黃公弼也到會場為小朋友們打氣。

今年參加的小朋友們程度都提高，九組中第一名取一位，第二名取二位，第三名取三位，自第一組到第九組名次排列是第一名吳澍祥、賴芝瑞、張浩君、陳示軼、董埼薇、韓人婷、周胤安、陳雪兒、及韓人蕙。第二名有宜睿奇與賴俊翰、陳必傑與王漢傑、董翰容與李佳陽、謝安琪與何佳、趙芝瑛與楊博海、陳朗與李佳鴻、蔡欣容與楊珮琳、賴傑瑞與杜庭瑤、楊謹嘉與簡貝函和、第三名有李昱芝與董琬馨和蔡聖齡、阮曉寧與王子云和阮曉柔、葛維雅與謝廷琪、廟宇葳與楊品琦和葛敏暉、王傑霖與盛孝華和劉祐竹、劉家玲與李小婕和葛敏雯、趙敏文與廟如涵和梁格、陳威達與古皓元和孫建祥、鄭芳怡與廟宇涵和王佑人，得獎的小朋友均獲得獎牌和獎金。

中華民國八十六年六月十四日　星期六

《NBA 總冠軍》

90：86 公牛蟬聯
NBA 總冠軍
喬丹五度膺選決賽最有價值球員

2. Read the news headline and answer the questions.
   a. What game is this?
   _____

   b. Which team won the championship? _____
   _____

   c. What was the final score? _____

   d. Jordan was elected as what? _____
   _____

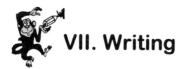

VII. Writing

A. Unscramble the following words into meaningful sentences.

1. 再過／我們／就要／考試了／一個星期

2. 他／一樣好／唱得／跟我／唱歌

3. 不如／看小說／有意思／看電視

4. 不如一天／老王的英文／一天／說得

B. Write a note to invite your friend to play golf this weekend. Apologize for not having been able to go with him/her last time due to a midterm and a paper.

YOU ARE INVITED...
Who: Andrew Chan
Where: Country Club
When: Saturday, March 15
Time: 2 p.m.

Call 822-8369

第二十課 你有沒有發燒？

I. Vocabulary

A. Write the meaning of the words and group them into two categories. Give each category a heading and explain it to your classmates, e.g., *Past Word*s: 醫生 (I was sick last week.) *Present Words:* 同屋兒 (I have a roommate now.)

1.	kōngqì	空氣	air _____
2.	dǎzhēn	打針	_____
3.	fāshāo	發燒	_____
4.	liángshuǐ	涼水	_____
5.	gǎnmào	感冒	_____
6.	kànbìng	看病	_____
7.	guòmǐn	過敏	_____
8.	nánshòu	難受	_____

1.		Reasons
2.		

B. Cross out the word that does not belong in the group.

1. 藥方、眼藥、萬金油、涼水、鐵打藥

2. 眼睛、鼻涕、兔子、腿、臉、頭髮

3. 紅、青、藍、癢、紫、黑、咖啡

C. Choose the appropriate word(s) to complete the following sentences.

1. Zuó.tiān wǒ (shuāi, fàn, shāng) .le yì jiāo, tuǐ.shàng qīng yí kuài, zǐ yí kuài .de.

   昨天我(摔、犯、傷)了一跤，腿上青一塊、紫一塊的。

2. Nǐ yīnggāi (zǎojiù, piānpiān, ànshí) chīyào, bìng cái huì hǎo.

   你應該(早就、偏偏、按時)吃藥，病才會好。

3. Nǐ yóu.méiyǒu (píqì, fǎ.zi, jièkǒu) bāng wǒ .de máng, zhè .ge (máo.bìng, wèntí, qíngkuàng) bù xiǎo.

   你有沒有(脾氣、法子、藉口)幫我的忙，這個(毛病、問題、情況)不小。

4. Tā zhěngtiān (chuīfēng, bàoyuàn, suānténg), nánguài méi rén xǐ.huān tā.

   他整天(吹風、抱怨、酸疼)，難怪沒人喜歡他。

II. Characters

Hàn zì	吹	風	病	疼	熱	涼	舒	服	約	醫
Notes	chuī to blow 7	fēng wind 9	bìng ill 7	téng ache 12	rè hot 15	liáng cool 11	shū relax 12	fú clothing 8	yuē appoint-ment 9	yī to cure 18
1										
2										
3										
4										
5										
6										

Compound/Phrase/Sentence/Journal/Memory Aid

吹	
風	
病	
疼	
熱	
涼	
舒	
服	
約	
醫	

Hàn zì	藥	法	讓	眼	睛	紅	同	屋	倒	題
Notes	yào medicine 19	fǎ method 8	ràng to let 24	yǎn eyes 11	jīng pupil 13	hóng red 9	tóng the same 6	wū room 9	dǎo to fall over 10	tí topic 18
1										
2										
3										
4										
5										
6										

	Compound/Phrase/Sentence/Journal/Memory Aid
藥	
法	
讓	
眼	
睛	
紅	
同	
屋	
倒	
題	

SVO

III. Grammar

🅐 Major Sentence Patterns

1. The co-verbs 叫 and 讓

S_1 叫/ 讓 O_1/S_2 (別/不要) V_2 O_2	S_1 let/tell O_1/S_2 (don't) V_2 O_2

1. 生病的時候，醫生讓你做什麼？

   _____

2. 老師為什麼讓你多聽錄音帶？

   _____

3. 來上大學的時候，你父母叫你別做什麼？

   _____

🅑 Usage of Common Phrases

1. The usage of 約

A (想/要) 約 B Time Exp. (在 Place) VO	A (would/will make) made an appointment with B to VO at Time Exp. (at Place)
A 跟 B 約好 Time Exp. (在 Place) VO	A made an appointment with B to VO at Time Exp. (at Place)

1. 你跟同屋約了什麼時候去打球？

   _____

2. 你要約誰跟你一塊兒去看電影、逛街？

   _____

3. 你學習有問題的時候，會怎麼做？

   _____

2. The preposition 從

從 S VO/Time Expression 以後, (S) 就 ...	S... ever since...
S 從 VO/Time Expression 以後, (S) 就 ...	

1. 你什麼時候開始對中文有興趣？

　　_____

2. 你什麼時候開始不吃肉的？

　　_____

4/3-4/5

3. 他感冒、發燒已經多久了？

　　_____

3. The interrogative adverb 多

多 SV?	How Adj (is...)?
多久/ 多好/ 多重?	How long/ good/ heavy (is...)?

1. 你學中文學了多久了？

　　_____

2. 你多重？要不要減肥？

　　_____

3. Michael Jordan 籃球打得多好？

　　_____

4. A 對 B 過敏

A 對 B 過敏	A is allergic to B

1. 你對什麼東西過敏？

　　_____

2. 你爲什麼不吃中國飯？

　　_____

3. 你爲什麼一直流鼻涕？

　　_____

5. The adverb 只是

| S 只是... | It is only the case that... |

1. 你要買東西嗎？(only take a look)

不，_____

2. 你不舒服嗎？(only a bit tired)

不，_____

3. 你好像哭了的樣子？(Some dust got into my eyes.)

沒什麼，_____

6. More on the co-verb 給

A 給 B 打針	A gěi B dǎzhēn	A gives B a shot
A 給 B 點眼藥	A gěi B diǎn yǎnyào	A applies eyedrops for B
A 給 B 量血壓	A gěi B liáng xuěyā	A checks B's blood pressure
A 給 B 看病	A gěi B kànbìng	A examines B
A 給 B 開藥方	A gei B kāi yàofāng	A writes a prescription for B

1. 你給醫生看病的時候，醫生會做什麼？

_____

2. 你病得很重的時候，醫生會做什麼？

_____

3. 你眼睛紅的時候，誰給你點眼藥？

_____

7. The usage of 打噴嚏

| S (一直)打噴嚏 | S (yìzhí) dǎ pēntì | S keeps sneezing |
| S 打了 (# 聲) 噴嚏 | S dǎ.le (# shēng) pēntì | S has sneezed no. of times |

1. 你整天打噴嚏，爲什麼不看醫生呢？

_____

2. 他怎麼了？

_____

8. 難受 **vs.** 難過

S 覺得 O 很/Adv 難受	S feels that O is very/Adv unbearable/intolerable/bad
S Adj 得 很/Adv 難受	S is so Adj that (S feels) uncomfortable
S 覺得　很/Adv 難過	S feels very/Adv sorry/bad/uncomfortable

1. 你難過的時候，會做些什麼？

_____

2. 什麼時候你會覺得很難過？

_____

3. 你的眼睛怎麼了？

_____

4. 什麼會讓你很難受？

_____

 IV. Listening

1. Which one is true?
   a. Xiao Wang caught a cold; she made an appointment to see a doctor yesterday.
   b. Xiao Lin caught a cold; she made an appointment to see a doctor tomorrow afternoon.
   c. Both Xiao Wang and Xiao Lin caught a cold; they made an appointment to see a doctor tomorrow afternoon.

2. Which one is true?
   a. The patient is fine; he doesn't have any problem.
   b. The patient caught a severe cold; he needs to take medicine.
   c. The patient has an allergy; he needs only to apply eyedrops.

3. What has happened to Xiao Wang?
   a. She was injured playing basketball.
   b. She was injured playing tennis.

c. She was injured playing football.
d. She was injured playing volleyball.

4. What was Xiao Lin's suggestion to Xiao Wang?
a. Go to see the doctor.
b. Apply some Tiger Balm herself.
c. Massage herself.
d. Take some painkiller.

 V. Speaking

A. Talk about yourself
Use the following questions as cues.
1. 你這個學期有沒有生病？你生了什麼病？

2. 你病了的時候，會做些什麼？

3. 什麼會讓你生病？你會過敏嗎？對什麼東西過敏？

4. 你有沒有什麼「老毛病」？

B. Role-play
1. You are 王華；call the doctor and tell him or her what's wrong with 美英.
2. You are at the clinic; tell the doctor what has been bothering you.
3. You are a doctor. A patient tells you what's wrong. You explain what you will do to help him/her get better.

C. I'm sick
Everyone in the class has a health problem today. Use your imagination and decide what your problem is. Move around the classroom and talk about your problem with your classmates. Show concern for each other and offer your advice.

D. Cultural differences
Talk to a foreign student or a Chinese and ask what kind of traditional treatments people get when they are not feeling well. Find out what kind of medicine they take.

VI. Reading

A. Read the Text

Check your comprehension of the lesson dialogue by deciding whether the statements are true or false.

T / F 1. Měiyīng gǎnmào .le, yīn.wèi tā yì dǎwán qiú jiù chuīfēng, hē liángshuǐ.

美英感冒了，因爲她一打完球就吹風、喝涼水。

T / F 2. Wánghuá quán shēn suānténg, tuǐ yě shāng .de qīng yí kuài, zǐ yí kuài .de.

王華全身酸疼，腿也傷得青一塊、紫一塊的。

T / F 3. Wáng Huá, Měiyīng dōu yào gěi yīshēng dǎ diànhuà, yuē shíjiān qù kànbìng.

王華、美英都要給醫生打電話，約時間去看病。

T / F 4. Měiyīng yìzhí liú bítì, dǎ pēn.tì, yǎn.jīng yòu yǎng yòu hóng.

美英一直流鼻涕、打噴嚏，眼睛又癢又紅。

T / F 5. Měiyīng tóuténg, fāshāo yǐ.jīng yí .ge duō xīng.qí .le.

美英頭疼、發燒已經一個多星期了。

T / F 6. Yī.shēng shuō Měiyīng chī .le yào, bìng hěn kuài jiù huì hǎo .de.

醫生說美英吃了藥，病很快就會好的。

T / F 7. Měiyīng duì kōngqì zhōng .de huīchén guòmǐn, děi dǎzhēn.

美英對空氣中的灰塵過敏，得打針。

T / F 8. Yī.shēng shuō Měiyīng .de wèntí bú dà, bú bì chī yào.

醫生說美英的問題不大，不必吃藥。

T / F 9. Yī.shēng yào Měiyīng liǎng .ge xīng.qí yǐ.hòu, zài lái kànbìng.

醫生要美英兩個星期以後，再來看病。

B. Read the Authentic Material

   1. Read the following advertisement, circle the words that you have learned, and find out what kind of illness this medicine is for.

   2. Read the following advertisement, circle the words that you have learned, and find out what kind of medical center it is and the business hours of this medical center.

華美中醫康復中心

1123 W. Argyle St. Chicago IL 60640
Tel: (312)271-0504 • Fax: (312)271-0503

上海中醫藥大學畢業(學制六年)
上海醫科大學中山醫院中醫教研室，教授著名中醫
師鄒揚華積四十年臨床經驗，精通中醫内外婦、針
灸、癌症、腫瘤等疑難雜症、心血管疾病、糖尿
病、高血壓、肝、膽、胃、腸疾病、腎炎、鼻炎、
皮炎、紅斑狼瘡、風濕性關節炎、肩周炎、男子性
功能不全、月經不調、不孕症。

就診時間：每日上午 10 時至下午 5 時

VII. Writing

A. Unscramble the following words into meaningful sentences.

1. 打了個電話／他／去看病／約好／醫生／給

2. 青一塊／我／不舒服／他／腿摔得／覺得／紫一塊的／也好不到哪兒去

3. 開了個藥方／給／醫生／他／打了一針

4. 再來看／吃一點兒藥／我／過兩個星期／你／還不好

B. Write a note (請假單子 qǐngjià dān.zi) to your teacher telling him/her that you have been sick for one week due to a severe flu and your doctor told you to stay in bed for a few days. Ask your teacher for sick leave (請病假 qǐng bìngjià) and permission to make up all the missed homework and quizzes when you recover. Use the patterns below:
1. S 從…以後，就…　　2. A 給 B 看病　　3. S₁ 叫 S₂ 別 V O

第二十一課 你要寄平郵還是快信？

 I. Vocabulary

A. Explain the meaning of the following words in Chinese.

1. yóujú   郵局   _____
2. dǎoyóu   導遊   _____
3. diàn.zixìn 電子信   _____
4. miǎnfèi   免費   _____

B. Word train
Think of words that include one of the characters or radicals in the compound that precedes it, e.g., 郵局→郵票→車票→車子

1. 存錢→ _____ → _____ → _____ → _____
2. 快信→ _____ → _____ → _____ → _____
3. 國内→ _____ → _____ → _____ → _____
4. 盒子→ _____ → _____ → _____ → _____

C. Choose the word/phrase from the parentheses that paraphrases the italicized word/phrase in the sentence.

1. Tā zhè .ge rén *zhēn gòu péng.yǒu.* (péng.yǒu hěn duō, yǒu hěn duō zhēn .de péng.yǒu, zhēn shì hǎo péng.yǒu)

    他這個人真夠朋友。(朋友很多、有很多真的朋友 、真是好朋友)

2. Yǐhòu nǐ xiǎng *dāng* shén.me? (tì, zuò, lǐng)

    以後你想當什麼？(替 、做 、領)

3. Nǐ chū.qù .de shí.hòu, qǐng *shùnbiàn* tì wǒ jì zhè fēng xìn. (hǎohāor .de, zhēn qiǎo, yí kuàir)

    你出去的時候，請順便替我寄這封信。(好好兒地 、真巧 、一塊兒)

4. Zuó.tiān wǒ zài jiē.shàng *pèng.jiàn* tā, tā zhèng zhǔnbèi dào yínháng qù. (kàn.jiàn, pèng.dào, tōngzhī)

    昨天我在街上踫見他，他正準備到銀行去。(看見 、踫到 、通知)

5. Tā yí fàng chūnjià, *mǎ.shàng* jiù zǒu. (lìkè, shàngmǎ, shànglái)

    他一放春假，馬上就走。(立刻 、上馬 、上來)

II. Characters

Hàn zì	存	提	擔	些	寄	封	郵	票	替	拿
Notes	cún to deposit 6	tí to carry 12	dān to shoulder 16	xiē some 8	jì to mail 11	fēng M for letter 9	yóu mail 12	piào ticket 11	tì to replace 12	ná to take 10
1										
2										
3										
4										
5										
6										

	Compound/Phrase/Sentence/Journal/Memory Aid
存	
提	
擔	
些	
寄	
封	
郵	
票	
替	
拿	

Hàn zì	帶	掛	遠	離	飛	機	場	馬	共	碰
Notes	dài belt 11	guà to hang 11	yuǎn far 14	lí away from 19	fēi to fly 9	jī machinery 16	chǎng open space 12	mǎ horse 10	gòng together 6	pèng to bump 13
1										
2										
3										
4										
5										
6										

	Compound/Phrase/Sentence/Journal/Memory Aid
帶	
掛	
遠	
離	
飛	
機	
場	
馬	
共	
碰	

III. Grammar

A Major Sentence Patterns

1. The adverb 正

S 正 V₁/AuxV V₂ O 呢	S is in the midst of Ving to V₂ O

1. 你現在要上哪兒去？

_____

2. 你來我家一下，好嗎？(I was about to go there and look for you.)

_____

3. 咱們出去吃飯怎麼樣？(I'm about to cook.)

    不必了，_____

2. The co-verb 用

S 用 X V O (instrument)	S V O with/by X

1. 你平常用什麼寫報告？用什麼寫信？

_____

2. 什麼人用手吃飯？中國人用什麼吃飯？美國人呢？

_____

3. 傳統的中國人用什麼寫字？用什麼畫畫兒？

_____

3. 不但..., 而且/ 並且 ...construction

S 不但..., 而且/ 並且也 ...	S not only..., but also...

1. 你覺得這兒的中國雜貨店怎麼樣？

_____

2. 春假的時候，咱們開車出去玩兒怎麼樣？

_____

3. 你覺得「喜福會」這部電影怎麼樣？

_____

4. Expressions of distance

4.1 A is far from/close to B

A 離 B 遠不遠？	Is A far from B?
A 離 B 近不近？	Is A close to B?
A 離 B 很/Adv 遠/近	A is very/Adv far from/close to B
A 離 B 不(太) 遠/近	A is not (very) far from/close to B
A 離 B 遠嗎？	Is A far from B?
A 離 B 遠/近得很	A is very far from/close to B
A 離 B 遠/近極了	A is extremely far from/close to B
A 離 B 有多遠？	How far is A from B?
A 離 B 有 no. 哩路	A is no. of miles from B

1. 你家離學校遠不遠？

_____

2. 圖書館離你家遠嗎？

_____

3. 這兒離芝加哥近不近？離舊金山呢？

_____

4. 印地 'Indianapolis' 離這兒有多遠？

	布城
印地	60 哩
芝加哥	300 哩
紐約	790 哩
舊金山	2,300 哩

5. Comparison of distance

5.1 比 comparison

A 離 C 比 B 離 C (還) 遠嗎？	Is A (still) farther from C than B is?
A 離 C 比 B 離 C (還) 近嗎？	Is A (still) closer to C than B is?

A 離 C 比 B 離 C（還）遠	A is (still) farther from C than B is
A 離 C 比 B 離 C（還）近	A is (still) closer to C than B is
A 離 C 比 B 離 C 遠一點兒	A is a little bit farther from C than B is
A 離 C 比 B 離 C 近一點兒	A is a little bit closer to C than B is
A 離 C 比 B 離 C 遠得多嗎？	Is A much farther from C than B is?
A 離 C 比 B 離 C 近得多嗎？	Is A much closer to C than B is?
A 離 C 比 B 離 C 遠得多了	A is much farther from C than B is
A 離 C 比 B 離 C 近得多了	A is much closer to C than B is

You want to go to a scenic spot for spring break. On the map, locate where you are now and the four places pictured. Write and answer three questions for your friends comparing the distances. You will go by rental car with a limit of 1,600 miles.

1. Q_____

   A_____

2. Q_____

   A_____

3. Q_____

   A_____

5.2 and 5.3 Equaling-degree and equal-degree comparison

A 離 C 有沒有 B 離 C 那麼/這麼 遠？	Is A as far from C as B is?
A 離 C 有沒有 B 離 C 那麼/這麼 近？	Is A as near to C as B is?
A 離 C 沒有 B 離 C　那麼/這麼 遠	A is not as far from C as B is
A 離 C 沒有 B 離 C　那麼/這麼 近	A is not as near to C as B is
A 離 C 跟 B 離 C　一樣 遠	A is about as far from/close to C as B is
A 離 C 跟 B 離 C　一樣 近	A is about as close to C as B is
A 離 C 跟 B 離 C 不一樣 遠	A is not as far from/close to C as B is
A 離 C 跟 B 離 C 不一樣 近	A is not as close to C as B is
A 離 C 不跟 B 離 C 一樣 遠	A and B are not equally far from C
A 離 C 不跟 B 離 C 一樣 近	A and B are not equally close to C

Compare apartment A and B based on the
information given in the table. Decide which
one you want to rent and provide at least
three reasons.

離	書店	圖書館	教室
A 公寓	五哩路	十五哩	九哩路
B 公寓	五哩路	三哩路	六哩路

1. 我要租＿＿＿＿ 因為

_____

_____

_____

6. The co-verb/verb 帶

S (Neg) (AuxV) 帶 O A(Neg) (AuxV) 帶 B 到 Place 去/來 VO S (Neg) (AuxV) 帶 O 到 Place 去/來 V(O)	S (AuxV) (Neg) brings O A (AuxV) (Neg) brings B along to Place to VO S (AuxV) (Neg) brings O to Place to V
S (Neg) (AuxV) 帶孩子 S (Neg) (AuxV) 帶路	S (AuxV) (Neg) takes care of a child S (AuxV) (Neg) leads the way

1. 你明天要帶什麼來慶祝他的生日？

_____

2. 你要帶我上哪兒去打高爾夫球？

_____

3. 為什麼孩子一看到她就笑了？

_____

4. 你要我幫什麼忙，說吧！ (I have never been to Chicago. May I follow you there?)

_____

7. The co-verb/verb 替

A (Neg) (AuxV) 替 B VO	A (AuxV) (Neg) in place of B to VO
A (Neg) (AuxV) 替 B VO	A (AuxV) (Neg) VO for B

1. 你生病的時候，誰替你去學校交功課？

_____

2. 你媽媽天天替你們做什麼？

_____

3. 他對你這麼不好，你為什麼還替他說好話？

_____

4. 你為什麼替他寫報告？

_____

 IV. Listening

1. How far is it from A's home to the school?
   a. It's very far, about 50 miles.
   b. It's very close, only 2.5 miles.
   c. It's not very far, about 5 miles.

2. What did B do yesterday?
   a. B went to the supermarket to buy groceries.
   b. B went to the post office to send a package.
   c. B went to the post office to pick up a package and buy some stamps.

3. Why doesn't Lin write letters to his parents very often?
   a. Because it takes a long time for letters to reach them.
   b. Because the postage is very expensive.
   c. Because writing letters is very time consuming.
   d. Because writing letters is not easy.

4. Which is true based on the dialogue?
   a. E-mail is free and quick.
   b. There is no need to use stationery and envelopes when sending e-mail.
   c. It's safer to send e-mail.
   d. B doesn't like to write letters.

5. Where does the conversation occur?
   a. Supermarket.
   b. Store.
   c. Theater.
   d. Bank.

V. Speaking

A. Talk about yourself
Use the following questions as cues.
1. 你喜歡寫信回家還是打電話回家？為什麼？

2. 你去過東方雜貨店嗎？那兒跟超級市場有什麼不同？

3. 你用過電子信嗎？用電子信有什麼好的、不好的地方？

4. 你替別人說過好話嗎？你當過導遊嗎？請說說你的經驗(jīngyàn 'experience')。

B. Role-play
1. Take the part of a customer who would like to send an airmail letter to China and a birthday gift to a relative/friend in Taiwan. Ask how much the postage will be for express and regular mail and how long it will take.

2. You just received a paycheck (薪水 xīnshuǐ)/ money order (匯票 huìpiào) of $500 and you would like to cash $200 and deposit $300.

3. You are a poor student and don't have money to pay for your tuition. You go to the bank to apply for a student loan (學生貨款 xué.shēng dàikuǎn). Tell the clerk that you need to borrow $3,000 and you'll pay back $100 per month.

C. Culture experience
1. Go to an Oriental grocery store to do some shopping. See if you can talk to the store owner in simple Chinese.
2. Ask a foreign student whether people in his/her country like to save money or not, and how he/she feels about the American way of spending money.
3. Talk to a Chinese person to learn more sayings like 天下父母心 and share them with your classmates.

	Saying	Meaning
1.		
2.		
3.		
4.		

VI. Reading

A. Read the Text

Check your comprehension of the lesson dialogue by answering the following questions.

1. Lǐ Míng yào shàng nǎr qù? Qù zuò shén.me?　李明要上哪兒去？去做什麼？

_____

2. Lǐ Míng .de fùmǔ wèishén.me lǎo gěi tā jì　李明的父母爲什麼老給他寄東西
   dōng.xī lái?　來？

_____

3. Wèishén.me Wáng Huá shuō "tiānxià fùmǔ　爲什麼王華說「天下父母心」？
   xīn?"

_____

4. Yóuwùyuán shuō Lǐ Míng .de bāoguǒ yǒu　郵務員說李明的包裹有什麼問題
   shén.me wèntí?　？

_____

5. Lǐ Míng juédìng jì píngyóu hái.shì kuàixìn?　李明決定寄平郵還是快信？爲什
   Wèishén.me?　麼？

_____

6. Fā diànzǐxìn yǒu shén.me hǎochù　發電子信有什麼好處？
   'advantage'?

_____

7. Wáng Huá shàng yínháng qù zuò shén.me?　王華上銀行做什麼？高德中呢？
   Gāo Dézhōng .ne?

_____

8. Gāo Dézhōng hé Lǐ Míng chūnjià .de　高德中和李明春假的時候，上哪
   shí.hòu, shàng nǎr qù .le? Wèishén.me?　兒去了？爲什麼？

_____

9. Gāo Dézhōng wèishén.me shuō Wáng Huá　高德中爲什麼說王華「夠朋友」？
   "gòu péng.yǒu?"

_____

B. Read the Authentic Material

1. Read the subscription form on the right and figure out:

a. If you are in Taiwan and want to receive the magazine by regular mail, how much does it cost for a one-year subscription?

_____

b. If you are in Hong Kong and want a lower subscription fee, how would the magazine be sent to you?

_____

請 存 款 人 注 意

一、如須限時存款請於存款單上貼足「限時專送」資費郵票

二、每筆存款至少須在新臺幣一元以上但存款尾數不在此限

三、倘金額誤寫請另換存款單填寫

四、本存款單不得附寄其他文件

訂閱價格

類　別		郵寄方式	訂　　價
國　內		平　寄	一年1450元（如需掛號另加120元）
國外訂閱（含郵費）	港澳地區	水　陸	NT$1750元（US$63元）
		航　空	NT$2750元（US$98元）
	亞洲大洋洲	水　陸	NT$2000元（US$71元）
		航　空	NT$3100元（US$111元）
	歐美非地區	水　陸	NT$2000元（US$71元）
		航　空	NT$3400元（US$121元）

◎國外掛號全年NT$288元（US$10元）

c. If you are an overseas subscriber and want the magazine sent to you by registered mail, how much extra do you have to pay? _____

通 信 欄

□新訂戶 □續訂戶　訂戶編號ＵＮ_____

（為了您的權益，續訂戶請務必註明）

◎訂閱人：請用正楷詳細填寫

姓名：_____　性別：□男□女

出生日期：____年____月____日

學歷：□大學以上 □大學專科 □高中職 □國中

地址：_____

_____

電話：_____　職業：_____

◎訂閱「聯合文學」雜誌

自____年____月起至____年____月止

□一年訂費1450元　□二年訂費2800元

□續訂一年1250元　□續訂二年2400元

若須掛號國內全年NT$120元

□訂贈大陸親友 —一年訂費2600元

收件人姓名：_____

地址：_____

2. Read the subscription form on the left and figure out:

a. If you are a new customer, how much does it cost to subscribe to the magazine for one year?

_____

b. If you want to continue your subscription for two years, how much does it cost? _____

c. If you want to subscribe to the magazine for your friends in mainland China, how much does it cost? _____

3. Read the following Chinese letter[1] and

    a. See how much of it you can understand.

    b. Circle the words that you haven't learned yet, ask your teacher for the pronunciations, and look them up in the dictionary.

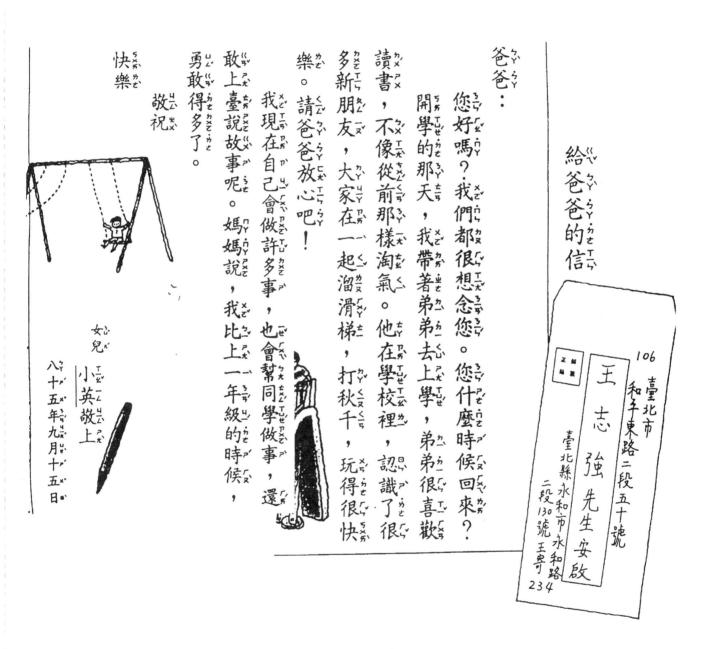

給爸爸的信

爸爸：

您好嗎？我們都很想念您。您什麼時候回來？

開學的那天，我帶著弟弟去上學，弟弟很喜歡讀書，不像從前那樣淘氣。他在學校裡，認識了很多新朋友，大家在一起溜滑梯，打秋千，玩得很快樂。請爸爸放心吧！

我現在自己會做許多事，也會幫同學做事，還敢上臺說故事呢。媽媽說，我比上一年級的時候，勇敢得多了。

敬祝

快樂

女兒 小英 敬上

八十五年九月十五日

106
臺北市和平東路二段五十號
王志強 先生安啟
臺北縣永和市永和路二段130號 王寄 234

[1] This is from 國民小學二年級上學期國語課本. By 國立編譯館, 台北, 1996.

VII. Writing

A. Choose a form to fill out pretending you are in mainland China or Taiwan. You want to deposit $1,538.00 in the bank.

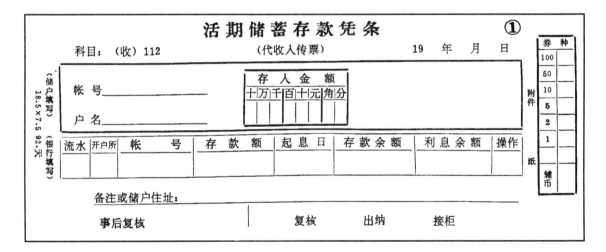

B. Complete the letter (at least 8 sentences) and envelope (address: 台北市大安區三民路一段五巷十弄七號) for Wang Hua in a traditional format. Tell her parents (王世民先生) that

1. She has received the check they recently sent her.
2. She fell recently when playing tennis with her roommate and got bruises all over her leg. Fortunately, she hasn't had hayfever or a cold.
3. She is doing well with her study and has gotten used to American life except for the food. She will start preparing for her final exams soon.

郵票
正貼

市縣
鄉鎮
市區
路（街）
段　巷　弄　號

縣市
鄉鎮
市區
路（街）
段　巷　弄　號　緘

第二十二課 我的車怎麼不見了？

 I. Vocabulary

A. Cross out the word that does not belong in the group.

1. 警察   化妝   執照   罰單   追
    jǐngchá   huàzhuāng   zhízhào   fádān   zhuī

2. 一定   八成   萬一   可能
    yídìng   bāchéng   wànyī   kěnéng

3. 駕駛   時速   停車   出事兒   準備
    jiàshǐ   shísù   tíngchē   chū shìr   zhǔnbèi

B. Word Association
   Think of words that you associate with the preceding words, e.g., 要求→ 老師→ 功課→
   累 → 休息→ 咖啡

1. 輪胎 → _____ → _____ → _____ → _____ → _____
2. 真糟糕 → _____ → _____ → _____ → _____ → _____
3. 怎麼辦 → _____ → _____ → _____ → _____ → _____
4. 發現→ _____ → _____ → _____ → _____ → _____

C. Choose the appropriate word to complete the following sentences.

1. Shàng.cì wǒ shuō, zhè.cì (dāng, gāi, yòng)
    nǐ .le.

    上次我說，這次 (當 、 該 、 用) 你
    了。

2. Tā shuō zhèr (búdàn, bùqiǎo, bùxǔ)
    chōuyān.

    她說這兒 (不但 、 不巧 、 不許) 抽
    煙。

3. Duì.bùqǐ, wǒ bǎ shí.jiān (búcuò, jìcuò,
    bújiàn) .le, wǒ yīnggāi zǎo diǎnr lái.

    對不起，我把時間 (不錯 、 記錯 、 不
    見) 了，我應該早點兒來。

4. (Xiǎo.xīn, Lìhài, Zhāojí) yì.diǎnr, bié bǎ
    hé.zi nòngpò .le.

    (小心 、 厲害 、 著急) 一點兒，別把盒
    子弄破了。

II. Characters 　　　　　　　　　　　　　　　　　　**Worksheet 38**

Hàn zì	求	借	單	位	剛	許	改	句	緊	張
Notes	qiú to seek 7	jiè to borrow 10	dān single 12	wèi M 7	gāng just 10	xǔ to permit 11	gǎi to change 7	jù sentence 5	jǐn tight 14	zhāng M 11
1										
2										
3										
4										
5										
6										

	Compound/Phrase/Sentence/Journal/Memory Aid
求	
借	
單	
位	
剛	
許	
改	
句	
緊	
張	

Hàn zì	腿	輕	千	萬	照	辦	總	非	被	陪
Notes	tuǐ leg 14	qīng light 14	qiān 1,000 3	wàn 10,000 13	zhào to shine 13	bàn to do 16	zǒng always 17	fēi is not 8	bèi by 10	péi accompany 11
1										
2										
3										
4										
5										
6										

	Compound/Phrase/Sentence/Journal/Memory Aid
腿	
輕	
千	
萬	
照	
辦	
總	
非	
被	
陪	

SVO

III. Grammar

Ⓐ Major Sentence Patterns

1. The usage of 借

1.1 借 as "to borrow...from"

| A (Neg) (AuxV) 跟 B 借 X | A (AuxV) (Neg) borrows X from B |

1. 你昨天沒去上課，得怎麼辦？(to borrow notes from my classmates)

_____

2. 你明天要去考車，可是你沒有車怎麼辦？

_____

3. 下個星期你得交報告，怎麼辦？

_____

1.2 and 1.3 借/ 把 X 借給 as "to lend...to"

| A (Neg) (AuxV) 借 X 給 B
 A (Neg) (AuxV) 借 給 B X | A (AuxV) (Neg) lends X to B |
| A (Neg) (AuxV) 把 X 借 給 B | A (AuxV) (Neg) lends X to B |

1. 你能不能借電腦給我？ (No, I can't. It's too expensive.)

_____

2. _____

可以，可是我的字典很小。

3. _____

可以，可是我的輪胎沒氣了。

2. 一邊兒... 一邊兒... construction

| S 一邊兒 V_1O_1，一邊兒 V_2O_2 | While one is Ving O_1, he/she is Ving O_2 |

1. 你總是一邊兒上課，一邊兒吃東西嗎？

_____

2. 你每天早上一邊兒喝咖啡，一邊兒做什麼？

_____

3. 你做功課的時候專心嗎？

不太專心， _____

3. The passive marker 被

A 被 B V 了	A was ... by B

1. 小王的電腦怎麼了？

_____

小馬

2. 小李的車怎麼了？

_____

3. 小高寫的筆記怎麼了？

_____

B Usage of Common Phrases

1. The adverb 從來

S 從來(都)不 VO	S never VO
S 從來(都)沒 V 過 O	S has never V-ed O

1. 你去過北極(Běijí 'North Pole')嗎？

_____

2. 你看過法國電影嗎？

_____

3. 什麼東西你從來沒吃過？

_____

4. 你常給你的家人寫信嗎？ (I talk to them by phone.)

_____

2. The movable adverb 難道

難道　S　Neg VO 嗎？	Do you mean to say that...?/
S　難道　Neg VO 嗎？	Could it be possible that...?

1. 這個字很難，我想沒人懂。

_____

2. 他的這個毛病已經很久了，一直沒好。 (Do you mean to say that even the doctor has no way of curing it?)

_____

3. 這個情況很特別，我想沒人知道。 (Do you mean to say that even the police didn't know about it?)

_____

3. The reduplicated adverbs 偏偏 and 明明

S　偏(偏) VO	S　VO　deliberately
S　明明　VO	Clearly S V

You are a strong-minded person. Try to retort whenever people give advice.

1. 你別吸煙。

_____

2. 你別把車停在這兒。

_____

3. 你現在別喝涼水。

_____

4. 他說你事前沒有通知他，所以他不來。 (I did inform him.)

_____

5. 這個錯字你還沒改。 (I did correct it.)

 IV. Listening

1. What happened to Xiao Gao's car?
   a.   He lent it to Xiao Lin.
   b.   He sold his car.
   c.   His car was towed by the police.

2. What did Xiao Wang ask Xiao Lin to do?
   a. Xiao Wang wanted Xiao Lin to drive slower.
   b. Xiao Wang wanted Xiao Lin to drive faster.
   c. Xiao Wang asked Xiao Lin to pay more attention when she drives.

3. Which one is true about the conversation?
   a.   B is walking.
   b.   B is running.
   c.   B is driving a car.
   d.   B is riding a bicycle.

 V. Speaking

A.   Talk about yourself
     Use the following questions as cues.
     1. 你會開車嗎？你喜歡開什麼樣的車？為什麼？

     2. 你是怎麼學會開車的？你的教練是誰？他教你的方法好不好？

     3. 你覺得考車難不難？你是什麼時候拿到駕駛執照的？

     4. 你開車有沒有出過事兒？請說說你的經驗(jīngyàn 'experience')。

B. Reality check

Talk to your classmate to find out

1. Where and when you can park your car for free on campus, on the street, or downtown.
2. Which parking lot charges a parking fee and how much the fee is per hour/day.
3. How much it costs to park a car on the street or in a garage downtown.
4. Where is the best place in town to get cars repaired.
5. Which nearby gas station is the cheapest one.

C. A bad day

Tell your conversation partner the following:

1. Your car's engine (引擎 yǐnqíng) was broken (壞了 huài.le). You took it to the dealer (車行 chēháng) for repair (修理 xiūlǐ) and it was very expensive. It cost you $700 to repair the engine. Start your talk with something like 我的車子平常很好，没有問題，可是昨天我發現…

2. You got a $60 ticket for speeding on the highway (高速公路 gāosù gōnglù) yesterday. You were caught by the police while listening to music and not paying attention. Start with the phrase 我昨天真倒霉，吃了一張罰單…

 VI. Reading

A. Read the Text

Check your comprehension of the lesson dialogue by deciding whether the statements are true or false.

T / F　1.　Gāo Dézhōng wàng .le zìjǐ bǎ chē tíng zài nǎr.　　高德中忘了自己把車停在哪兒。

T / F　2.　Gāo Dézhōng měitiān dōu bǎ chē tíng zài yíyàng .de dì.fāng.　　高德中每天都把車停在一樣的地方。

T / F　3.　Gāo Dézhōng xiǎng tā .de chē bāchéng jiào rén gěi tuōzǒu .le.　　高德中想他的車八成叫人給拖走了。

T / F　4.　Lín Měiyīng xiǎng gēn Gāo Dézhōng jiè chē qù mǎi dōng.xī.　　林美英想跟高德中借車去買東西。

T / F　5.　Wáng Huá xiǎng ràng Měiyīng jiāo tā kāichē, péi tā liànchē.　　王華想讓美英教她開車，陪她練車。

T / F   6.   Wáng Huá kāichē .de shíhòu hěn
              jǐnzhāng.

王華開車的時候很緊張。

T / F   7.   Wáng Huá kāichē .de shí.hòu, bú
              gòu zhuānxīn yě bú gòu xiǎo.xīn.

王華開車的時候，不夠專心也不
夠小心。

T / F   8.   Měiyīng xǐ.huān yì biānr kāichē, yì
              biānr tīng yīnyuè, huàzhuāng.

美英喜歡一邊兒開車，一邊兒聽
音樂、化妝。

T / F   9.   Měiyīng jué.de Wáng Huá kāichē
              kāi .de tài màn .le.

美英覺得王華開車開得太慢了。

T / F   10. Wáng Huá jué.de Měiyīng shì .ge
              hǎo jiàoliàn.

王華覺得美英是個好教練。

B. Read the Authentic Material
   Read the following advertisement and answer the questions:

   1. What kind of advertisement is this? _____

       _____

   2. Can you guess what kind of services they do? _____

       _____

       _____

       _____

VII. Writing

A. Write the meaning of the following signs.

1. _____

2. _____

3. _____

4. _____

5. _____

6. _____

B. Unscramble the following words into meaningful sentences.

1. 警察／他／車／拖走了／的／被

2. 把／停／我／車／旁邊兒／平常／在學校

3. 快車／可／別開／容易／出事／要不然

4. 不能／小王／吃飯／念書／一邊兒／一邊兒

C. Place an ad on the bulletin board of the Student Center in your school stating that you are looking for a used Japanese car around $2,000. Outline the features you want.

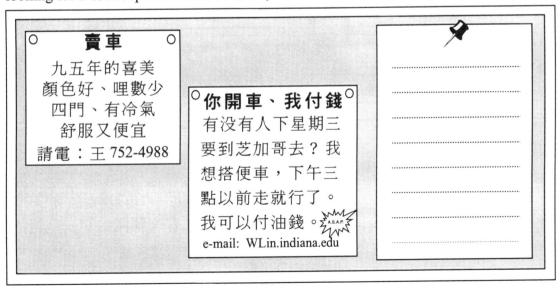

第二十三課 你們暑假打算做什麼？

I. Vocabulary

A. Complete the crossword puzzle with the cues given.

Across	Down
3. all day long	1. in case
5. tuition	2. scholarship
6. to go for a trip	4. evening
8. very rare	7. hotel
	8. sad

B. Write the meaning of the words and group them into two categories. Give each category a heading and explain it to your classmates, e.g., *Past Word*s: 加拿大 (I went to Canada last year.) *Future Words:* 夏天 (Summer is coming.)

1. shǔjià   暑假   _____
2. biǎomèi   表妹   _____
3. qīmòkǎo   期末考   _____
4. jìnbù   進步   _____
5. liáotiān   聊天   _____
6. lùyíng   露營   _____
7. shěngqián   省錢   _____
8. dānwù   耽誤   _____

1.	Reasons
2.	

C. Choose the appropriate word to complete the following sentences.

1. Nà .ge xuéxiào hěn guì, nǐ (shàng.buqǐ, shàng.deqǐ, shàng.dequ) .ma?

   那個學校很貴，你（上不起、上得起、上得去）嗎？

2. Tīngshuō zhèr .de shāngxuéyuàn yì nián zhǐ (ná, liú, shōu) shí .ge xué.shēng.

   聽說這兒的商學院一年只（拿、留、收）十個學生。

3. Zhè .ge bìyè diǎnlǐ hěn (nándé, nánguài, nánshuō), nǐ yīnggāi cānjiā.

   這個畢業典禮很（難得、難怪、難說），你應該參加。

II. Characters

Hàn zì	附	本	報	告	語	言	週	末	休	息
Notes	fù near to 8	běn root; origin 5	bào newspaper 12	gào tell 7	yǔ language 14	yán speech 7	zhōu week 12	mò end, last 5	xiū to rest 6	xí news 10
1										
2										
3										
4										
5										
6										

Compound/Phrase/Sentence/Journal/Memory Aid

附	
本	
報	
告	
語	
言	
週	
末	
休	
息	

Hàn zì	暑	底	妹	留	旅	費	已	經	驗	算
Notes	shǔ summer 13	dǐ underside 8	mèi younger sister 8	liú to keep 10	lǚ to travel 10	fèi expense 12	yǐ to stop 3	jīng to pass by 13	yàn to test 23	suàn to count 14
1										
2										
3										
4										
5										
6										

	Compound/Phrase/Sentence/Journal/Memory Aid
暑	
底	
妹	
留	
旅	
費	
已	
經	
驗	
算	

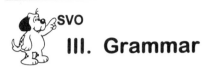

III. Grammar

Ⓐ Major Sentence Patterns

1. 先...然後... construction

S 先 (AuxV) V₁O₁，然後 V₂O₂ S (AuxV) 先 V₁O₁，然後 V₂O₂	S (AuxV) V₁ O₁ first, (and) then V₂ O₂

1. 放假以後你要上哪兒去？

   _____

2. 今天早上起床(qǐchuáng 'to get up')以後，你做了什麼？

   _____

3. 從波士頓(Bōshìdùn 'Boston')坐飛機到中國去，可能會停哪幾個地方？

   _____

2. More on 才 and 就

2.1 才 as "not until"

S Time Expression 才 VO	S will not VO until Time Expression (the action won't be done/occur until later time)

1. 你今年要到中國去嗎？

   _____

2. 你現在要給她寫信嗎？ (after final)

   _____

3. 下個月你得去實習嗎？

   不， _____

2.2 才 as "only"

S Time Expression 才 No. M	S will be only No. M on Time Expression (the number is lesser/smaller than expected)

1. 你們倆結婚幾年了？

1996

_____

2. 你在圖書館打工，一個小時可以賺多少錢？

_____

3. 你明天得交報告嗎？

_____

2.3/2.4 就 as "on/in time"

S Time Expression 就 VO 了	S has done VO on/in Time Expression (the action has already been done/occurred sooner than the expected time)
S Time Expression 就 No. M (N) 了	S was already No. M on/in Time Expression (the number is greater/larger than expected)

1. 你在這兒已經住了多久了？

_____

2. 你在這個學校學習已經幾年了？

_____

3. 你今年多大了？

_____

Ⓑ Usage of Common Phrases

1. The Chinese concept of location

Whole 》 Part	
X 東/西 部	the eastern/ western part of X
X 南/北 部	the southern/ northern part of X
X 東南 部	the southeastern part of X
X 東北 部	the northeastern part of X
X 西北 部	the northwestern part of X
X 西南 部	the southwestern part of X
X 中西 部	the midwestern part of X

1. 美國什麼地方最有意思？為什麼？

   _____

2. 美國什麼地方人最多？什麼地方牛比人多？

   _____

3. 中國什麼地方你最想去玩兒？為什麼？

   _____

2. VO 對 X 有幫助

VO 對 X (很) 有幫助	VingO is (very) helpful to X

1. 什麼對你學中文有幫助？

   _____

2. 出去實習對找工作有幫助嗎？

   _____

3. 看中國電影對明白中國社會有沒有幫助？

   _____

3. The complement 不得了

不得了！S V O 了	Good Heavens! S did...!
S SV 得不得了	S is extremely/awfully Adj

1. 你這幾天怎麼樣？

   _____

 2. 你的肚子怎麼了？

   _____

3. 你的頭怎麼了？

   _____

4. The successive aspect 下去

O…V　　下去	to continue Ving O
O…V 不下去	cannot continue Ving O

1. 中文你想學下去嗎？爲什麼？

　　_____

2. 請問，從這兒到大學書店怎麼走？ (go straight ahead)

　　_____

3. 從這兒走八十號公路(gōnglù 'highway')，會到哪兒？

　　_____

© Reentry

1. The differences between 的、地 、得

N₁/Pron 的 N	N₁'s N
(S) V 的 N	The N that (S) V
(Adv) Adj 的 N	(Adv) Adj N
Adj 的 (N)	The Adj one
V 的 (N)	The one (that X) did V
Adj Adj 地 V/Adj	Adj-ly
V 得 Comp	

Fill in the following blanks with 的、得 or 地

1. 下個月我要去參加我妹妹_____畢業典禮。

2. 下雪的時候，路很滑，要小心_____走。

3. 你的漢字寫_____怎麼樣？。

4. 昨天他摔了一跤，今他的腿疼_____很。

5. 他寫_____小說 很有意思。

6. 我們學校_____學費很貴。

7. 你要去旅行_____話，最好多帶一點兒錢。

8. 那本書是借_____，不是買_____。

9. 最近我忙_____不得了。

10. 在美國買_____到筷子嗎？

11. 坐在那兒 _____ 那個人是我 _____ 老師。他是東亞系 _____ 教授。他課教

_____ 很好，所以我們學 _____ 也很好，進步很大。但是他 _____ 要求有

一點兒高，他給我們很多功課，讓我們忙 _____ 沒時間休息。他總是說，

「你們上課以前，得好好 _____ 準備，上課 _____ 時候，要專心 _____ 聽

課。」有時候，他說 _____ 、問 _____ 都沒有人懂，但是他會慢慢兒

_____ 再說幾次，讓我們明白。他真是個好老師！

IV. Listening

1. B's final exam is:
   a. Next Friday.
   b. This Friday.
   c. Next Monday.
   d. This Monday.

2. A's summer plans are:
   a. To work in May and then go to see his parents.
   b. To go home first and then go to summer school.
   c. To go home first, and then go to New York to do an internship.
   d. To do internship and then go home to see his parents.

3. Which one is true about the dialogue?
   a. Xiao Li's parents can't come because they are too busy.
   b. Xiao Li's parents can't come because airplane tickets are too expensive.
   c. Xiao Li's parents won't come because his mother doesn't like to fly.
   d. Xiao Li's parents won't come because his mother doesn't know how to drive.

V. Speaking

A. Talk about yourself
   Use the following questions as cues.
   1. 你有沒有期末考？你什麼時候大考？大考的時候，你緊張不緊張？

   2. 你去年暑假做了什麼？今年你打算做什麼？

3. 你夏天的時候，想不想去哪兒走走？你會用什麼法子旅行呢？

4. 你覺得怎麼樣學習，對學生的語言水平有幫助？

5. 你什麼時候畢業？畢業以後，你打算做什麼？

B. Cultural difference
Exchange views with your Chinese friends with the help of following questions:
1. Do Americans value graduation ceremonies (high school, college)?   Why or why not?
2. Do Chinese value graduation ceremonies as much as Americans? Why or why not?
3. How do Chinese celebrate their graduations?

C. If I were rich …
Suppose you have a lot of money, what would you do with it? Would you go for a trip, pay for the tuition to attend a summer study program, or buy a gift for yourself and your family?
1. If you would like to travel, where will you go? By what means and why?
2. If you choose to study, which program would you apply to? Why?
3. If you choose to shop, what would you buy and for whom?

 # VI. Reading

A. Read the Text
Check your comprehension of the lesson dialogue by answering the following questions.

1. Wáng Huá zuìjìn zài máng shén.me?   王華最近在忙什麼？

_____

2. Lín Měiyīng zuìjìn zài máng shén.me?   林美英最近在忙什麼？

_____

3. Wáng Huá shǔjià .de shí.hòu, dǎsuàn zuò   王華暑假的時候，打算做什麼？
    shén.me?

_____

4. Lín Měiyīng shǔjià .de shíhòu, dǎsuàn zuò   林美英暑假的時候，打算做什麼？
    shén.me?

_____

5. Gāo Dézhōng dǎsuàn zěn.me lìyòng zhè .ge shǔjià?　　　高德中打算怎麼利用這個暑假？

_____

6. Wèishén.me Gāo Dézhōng shuō shàng qiánghuàbān .de shíhòu, bù néng yìbiānr dǎgōng, yìbiānr xuéxí?　　　為什麼高德中說上強化班的時候，不能一邊兒打工，一邊兒學習？

_____

7. Wáng Huá lái Měi.guó yǐhòu, tā .de Yīngwén zěn.meyàng .le?　　　王華來美國以後，她的英文怎麼樣了？

_____

8. Lǐ Míng shǔjià .de shíhòu, wèishén.me bù chū.qù lǚxíng?　　　李明暑假的時候，為什麼不出去旅行？

_____

9. Lín Měiyīng jué.de yí .ge rén qián bù duō, néng.bùnéng qù lǚxíng? Wèishén.me?　　　林美英覺得一個人錢不多，能不能去旅行？為什麼？

_____

B. Read the Authentic Material
   1. Read the following advertisement, and answer the questions.

      a. The airfare from Chicago to Italy is _____

      b. The airfare from Chicago to France is _____

      c. The airfare from Chicago to Germany is _____

      d. The languages the agents can speak are _____

藍天碧海萬里遨遊 最新推出

歐州最好玩價格最公道

芝加哥 .... 法國 $338(雙程)
芝加哥 .... 德國 $338(雙程)
芝加哥 .... 意大利 $338(雙程)

美國之旅大飽眼福

美東遊(紐約、華盛頓、尼加拉瀑布、大西洋)
美西遊(洛杉磯、舊金山、拉斯維加斯、大峽谷)
佛羅里達、夏威夷

精通國語、粤語、英語
代理西北、聯合、日航、中華、長榮、韓航、中國民航、東方航空及美國國内機票。

2. Read the following newspaper clipping and answer the questions.

   a. If you have only two weeks for vacation and you are interested in the Silk Road, which travel plan would you choose? _____

   b. If you want to visit Beijing, which travel plan would you choose? _____ How many days does it take? _____

   c. If you want to see as many cities in China as possible, which travel plan would you choose? _____ How many cities would you be able to see? _____ How much does it cost? _____

提前報名 優惠$100 華夏假期精選系列

A★十六天12大城市   豪華遊 $2499 精華遊 $2299
暢遊:上海、杭州、蘇州、無錫、鎮江、揚州、南京、北京、西安、桂林、廣州、香港

B★十六天黃山三峽昆明   豪華遊 $2699 精華遊 $2499
暢遊:上海、黃山、武漢、長江大小三峽、重慶、昆明、黃果樹瀑布、貴陽、
廣州、香港

C★十六天北京西安三峽桂林   豪華遊 $2699 精華遊 $2499
暢遊:北京、西安、武漢、長江大小三峽、重慶、桂林、廣州、香港

D★十一天上海黃山三峽   豪華遊 $2399 精華遊 $2199
暢遊:上海、黃山、武漢、長江大小三峽、重慶、廣州、香港

E★十一天絲綢之路   豪華遊 $2699 精華遊 $2499
暢遊:北京、烏魯木齊、吐魯番、敦煌、蘭州、大觀園

F★十一天5大精選城市   豪華遊 $2199 精華遊 $2099
暢遊:北京、西安、桂林、廣州、香港

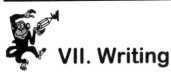

VII. Writing

A. Fill out the following form to apply for a study program in China.

北京语言文化大学（原北京语言学院）
来华留学生入学申请表

请申请人认真阅读本表的注意事项后再填写下列诸项：
Note:Do not complete this application without reading the instructions.

1. 姓名： _____ _____ _____	
2. 出生日期地点　　年 ____ 月 ____ 日 ____	照片
3. 国籍	4. 性别　男□　女□	

5. 通信地址及电话号码 _____ _____ _____	6. 婚姻　已婚□未婚□	7. 宗教信仰
	8. 护照号码	

9. 本人学历

校名	在学时间(年月～年月)	取得证书、学位	主要学习课目

请交学业证书影印件及正式成绩单,非中文或英文原件需附译件。

B. Write a letter (at least 8 sentences) to your parents commenting on your study of Chinese this year and describing your summer plans. Include the structures:
1. X Adj 得不得了
2. S Time Expression 才 VO
3. S Time Expression 就 VO 了
4. VO 對 X 有幫助
5. S 先…, 然後…